J. P. MARQUAND, ESQUIRE

A Portrait in the Form of a Novel

By Philip Hamburger

The Oblong Blur and Other Odysseys
J. P. Marquand, Esquire

J. P. MARQUAND
ESQUIRE

A Portrait in the
Form of a Novel

BY

PHILIP HAMBURGER

Charter Books

Charter edition published July, 1963

This book is the complete text of the hardcover edition

CHARTER BOOKS
Published by
THE BOBBS-MERRILL COMPANY, INC.
A subsidiary of HOWARD W. SAMS & CO., INC.
Publishers   Indianapolis and New York

Distributed by the Macfadden-Bartell Corp., Inc.,
205 East 42nd Street, New York 17, New York

To Edith

who makes wonderful coffee

The contents of this book
first appeared in *The New Yorker*

Contents

J. P. MARQUAND, ESQUIRE

A Portrait in the Form of a Novel

I'm No Good in the Morning
Till I've Had My Coffee

ALLISON CRAIG drank down his second cup of breakfast coffee and remarked to himself that even after eight years of marriage May had never quite learned the trick of making good coffee. To be sure, he drank two cups of whatever it was she brewed up each morning, for a man needed his coffee. Craig glanced over the top of his *Herald Tribune,* and across the green metal garden-style table that May had bought at Macy's last year for $39.98 ("I tell you, Allison, they *are* used indoors in dining rooms," she had said at the time. "There's one in this month's *House & Garden*"), at May, whose hair was still in pins, at Adam, six, and Susan, four, who were busily spooning cold cereal, at the orange chintz draperies framing the small, partitioned window that cranked in and out but not up and down, at the similar window across the

1

way in the similar apartment house — there were ten of them, all exactly alike, in this middle-income urban development — and suddenly it seemed to him that his morning coffee symbolized his life. The coffee was certainly not good, but it could not be described as entirely bad, either. May tried hard. She always tried. A month or so ago, she had experimented with a new brand of coffee she had seen advertised in an extravagantly illustrated magazine devoted to the culinary arts. "Just three days ago, this gleaming ebony bean lived placidly alongside its mates near the headwaters of the Amazon," the advertisement read. "Two days ago, it lay dockside in sunny Rio, readying itself for the swift and magical air ride northward. Yesterday, it was on the shelves of the finest food stores everywhere, and THIS MORNING, its zingy tanginess unimpaired, it starts off your day with a cheery, sincere hello." This special brand of coffee turned out to be the least palatable coffee Craig had ever tasted, and just last week May had abandoned it and returned to the medium-priced coffee sold at the A. & P. We're always coming back in the end to the medium-priced coffee at the A. & P., Craig thought.

May's struggle to please him with the coffee paralleled his own struggle with himself and his work. He dreamed often of leaving *Sweep*, the two-dollar-a-copy monthly on which he worked, and "going off to do a little creative writing of my own," but he had been there seven years, and no sooner had he finished one article than he found himself engaged in doing another. For some years now, he had tried to convince himself, before undertaking a new assignment, that this next one, like the coffee, would be the best one, if not the last, and that in some curious fashion it would change his whole life. But during the past year he had experienced an indefinable sense of what all the writers on *Sweep* called quiet desperation, and he was almost afraid to tell himself something he was almost certain that he knew — that he had gone about as far as he could go. Nonetheless, on this cold winter morning he once again felt the old, gnawing, turbulent sense of quest, the intimations of adventure and inquiry that seized him each time he started out in earnest on a new article. Craig enjoyed the temporary elevation of his spirits. The frustration and letdown would come later, he knew. They always did.

He had been assigned to write an article about John P. Marquand, the novelist. In a way, it was a choice assignment. Here, certainly, was a man Craig could admire, a novelist of distinction and grace. Craig knew next to nothing about Marquand personally — he had talked with him on the telephone a few days before, to make arrangements for meeting with him, and he had been struck by the singularly cultivated inflections of the man's voice — but for years he had seen Marquand's photograph on the dust jackets of his books, and the face was unlike that of any other writer Craig had ever seen, photographed or in person. One would take Marquand for the headmaster of some fine old New England school for boys. The close-cropped graying hair, the white severity of the mustache, the clear, cold, bright eyes, the pipe, the tweed jacket, and the conservative Brooks Brothers tie all bespoke respectability, tried and trusted values, an uncompromising attitude toward life, a release from inner turmoil and doubt. Craig could picture him, brandy glass in hand, sitting, surrounded by a few old friends, in the deep leather armchair of some fashionable club, or discussing with his agents and attorneys his tidily managed financial affairs, or addressing the boys at Haversham Hall on "What Has Happened to Honor?" But when, in his mind's eye, Craig tried to see Marquand seated before a blank sheet of paper, engaged with the muse, his imagination failed him. Craig, however, had interviewed enough people and written enough articles about them to know that you never could tell from a celebrated man's picture what sort of man he was. You never could tell even after you had met the man. That was the trouble. You never could tell.

One thing Craig did know. Marquand could write. He could write like a breeze. Craig had read some of the books long before he ever knew he would be assigned to write a story about Marquand, and since taking on the assignment he had read all the rest of the twenty-nine novels and serials, and had glanced through a good many of the hundred and ten short stories and articles. The short stories had been appearing in the popular magazines since 1922, and the novels, or at least the novels since Marquand's first great "serious" success, *The Late George Apley* (which brought him a Pulitzer Prize in 1938), had been hitting the bookstores approximately once every two years. They always made the best-seller lists. In fact, Marquand's latest, *Melville Goodwin, USA,* was high on the lists now; it had been lodged there since its publication, in the fall of 1951. A dramatization by Paul Osborn of his next-to-latest book *Point of No Return,* was playing to packed houses on Broadway. Everything Marquand touched seemed to turn to gold. Craig had looked up some of the sales figures, and they were staggering. A total of 1,542,547 copies of his books had been sold in cheap editions, and a total of 2,291,293 of his books had been sold in book-club editions, bringing his sales outside of regular trade sales to 3,833,840. Not that his regular trade sales were to be sneezed at. *So Little Time,* for example, had sold 231,166 copies; *B. F.'s Daughter* had sold 168,574 copies; *Point of No Return* had sold 129,118 copies. Prior to *The Late George Apley,* Marquand had written mostly serials and adventure stories for the *Saturday Evening Post* and other magazines; he had also been attached to a small, sibilant Japanese detective, Mr. Moto, but Mr. Moto's book sales were not great, hovering between three thousand and five thousand copies. *The Late George Apley* had been a critical and popular success, and 46,338 people had bought copies of the regular trade edition. The effect on Marquand had been astonishing. From that time forward, he had devoted himself to novels of contemporary American life, and although the long-haired critics were too preoccupied with Kafka and Henry James to pay much heed to a man who wrote readable social novels of his own era, the public seemed delighted with his work, and most of the day-to-day reviewers hailed him as one of the three or four most important American novelists of the day. The long-haired critics claimed that Marquand wrote with too much smoothness, but Craig had read somewhere that Marquand worried not a bit about their criticism and had once remarked, "I don't know anybody who's had a kind word to say for me since I was a small boy."

Craig put down his *Herald Tribune* and thought for a moment of the warm spot he felt in his heart for a good many of the Marquand novels. He thought of the gentle but biting satire of *The Late George Apley,* with its penetrating portrait of a dying Beacon Hill life. He thought of the nostalgic mood that had come over him when he read *Wickford Point,* that humorous study of a proud, eccentric old family holding on to an antique homestead in New England. He thought of the tenderness and comedy of *Point of No Return,* with its accurate picture of life in a fashionable New York bank, in the rich suburbs of New York, and (in a flashback to an earlier day) in a small town near Boston. Craig thought of *Melville Goodwin, USA,* too, and although he had found it overextended and wordy, he could not help admiring Marquand's meticulous study of a military man's mind, and the profusion of detail that had gone into the work. Craig admired this man who could stretch an essentially simple narrative to four or five hundred pages, and he had a certain awe of Marquand's method of shifting his scenes from the present to the remembered past without any noticeable grinding of gears. There were people down at *Sweep* who didn't like Marquand one bit. They said that he wrote the same story over and over again, that he was plotless and pointless, and that he would have done better to stick with Mr. Moto instead of writing those endless stories of the small-town boy who achieves success in the big city and finds success a stifling experience. But, as Craig had said to one of those fellows the other day, he gets it written, doesn't he, and even if it isn't all absolutely topnotch, some of it is. Craig also admired Marquand for his ability to gauge popular taste, and for having the courage to become a member of the board of judges of the Book-of-the-Month Club, although he was not entirely sure why he admired Marquand for this, except that he had heard there was twenty thousand a year in it.

Craig looked at his watch and whistled. Seven-forty! He was to meet Marquand aboard the eight-o'clock train for Boston — they had parlor-car seats — and travel with him to Newburyport, Massachusetts, Marquand's home town, where Marquand was to deliver a paper that evening before the Tuesday Night Club. Marquand had suggested the arrangement, feeling that Craig could get better acquainted with him in this manner than by just asking a lot of routine biographical questions.

"More coffee?" asked May.

"No time," said Craig.

"There's never any time," said May.

Craig took the two steps from the dining alcove to the foyer with a strange buoyancy. There was no escaping the fact that a day or two away from home and the office put new life into a man. Craig reached into the closet for his medium-priced gray fedora and his medium-priced gray overcoat, picked up the lightweight brown airplane suitcase he had left by the door the night before, called goodbye to the family (the children hardly looked up, while May looked up and quickly looked down again), and walked into the hall. I really love all of them very much, Craig thought. Things might have been different, but there's no turning back now. The elevator stopped at his floor and the door opened noiselessly. He entered the car, and the door closed noiselessly behind him. In the car, Craig felt like a trapped animal; he felt like a trapped animal so much of the time these days. He walked swiftly through the coldly functional lobby and onto the street, where he hailed a taxi. "Grand Central," he said.

2

There's Something About Your Face

JOHN P. MARQUAND awakened early in the apartment on East Sixty-Seventh Street, and experienced, even while dressing and fixing himself a light breakfast, a feeling of emptiness and loneliness. The feeling sprang in no way from the fact that he was alone in the apartment, for being alone there was one of the supreme joys of having a place in town — a place where one could think one's thoughts and get one's work done. Greenwich had its good points, to be sure, with Adelaide, and Adelaide's mother, Mrs. Hooker, and the three little children, and the governess, who wore out one clutch after another on the station wagon, but when you came right down to it, there was no repose in suburbia for a man of fifty-eight who also happened to be a writer. And the three little children — Blanche Ferry Marquand,

twelve; Timothy Fuller Marquand, ten; and Elon
Huntington Hooker Marquand, nine — were,
regardless of how much he loved them, a handful
for a man his age. They were more like grand-
children, really, and as he watched them grow
and observed their problems, he often recalled
how he had gone through the same thing years
ago with Christina and John, Jr., the children of
his first marriage. Christina and John were in
their twenties now, grown up and independent
— Christina married to a graduate student of
history at Harvard, living with her husband and
baby in a rambling house with a porch in Cambridge, and John, Jr., working hard on a novel
in New York. No, the feeling of loneliness arose
from something else, and now, standing in the
apartment, knotting his wine-colored wool tie,
he knew that it arose from the prospect of his trip
to Newburyport. No matter how often he went
back there — even when he stayed for months at
a time at his place on Kent's Island, a few miles
from Newburyport itself — he felt the loneliness
that comes over one when the past rushes through
the mind in a surging flood of memory. On this
cold winter morning in New York, he could see
himself, for a moment, as a lad in his teens,
dressed in his best dark suit, leaving the Yellow
House at Curzon's Mill, where he lived with his

aunts, walking beside the river to the trolley, taking the trolley into Newburyport, and walking
over to High Street (its fine old Federalist houses
framed in the powder blue of the evening light)
and into the house of Mr. L. P. Dodge. He had
come to ask Mr. Dodge for a scholarship to Harvard — one of the Harvard Club Scholarships,
for deserving Newburyport lads — and he was
shy and frightened, and he stood in a corner of
Mr. Dodge's parlor and never once looked him in
the eye. One was supposed to look people in the
eye; to look them in the eye denoted character,
initiative, resourcefulness — all the abiding virtues. But young Marquand felt a shame and em-
barrassment that he could not overcome, a sense
of acute pain at belonging to the poor branch of
a well-to-do family, at having to take that damn
streetcar into town, at attending Newburyport
High rather than one of the fancy preparatory
schools his cousins went to. He did not get the
scholarship, but he went on to Harvard anyway,
and then into the world, and tonight, perhaps
Newburyport's most celebrated son, he was to
deliver his paper before the Tuesday Night Club
in the home of that same Mr. L. P. Dodge.

This thought cheered Marquand somewhat
and, putting on his suit coat, he walked out of
the bedroom of the apartment and into the living

room, savoring the silence. Yes, the apartment in town was fine for a night or two alone. He had come down from Greenwich the morning before to attend a meeting of the judges of the Book-of-the-Month Club in its executive offices, on lower Sixth Avenue, and to spend an evening in town before catching an early train for Boston this morning with that man from *Sweep*, the one who was going to write the article about him. He really enjoyed those Book-of-the-Month Club meetings. The routine was always pretty much the same, and the atmosphere was easygoing and informal. The judges met, at lunchtime, in Board Chairman Harry Scherman's big, handsomely decorated office overlooking the Hudson River, to the west, and the midtown towers of Manhattan, to the north, and sat at a long table beneath a large oil painting of the judges. Dorothy Canfield Fisher, who was pictured in the group, was no longer a judge (her place had been taken by Amy Loveman), but all the rest were there, alert, and literary: good old Dr. Henry Seidel Canby, critic, historian, and friend; Clifton (Kip) Fadiman, quick-witted and brilliant; Christopher (Kit) Morley, with the leonine head and scraggly beard; Meredith Wood, president of the Club; Harry Scherman; and, of course, himself. The portrait was an accurate representation of the friendliness of their meetings, for it showed them at lunch, the inevitable oysters on the half shell before each place and the wine flowing discreetly. Kip was sipping some wine and Kit was draining his glass. Marquand, wearing a dark-blue shirt, had his eyes on a plate of rolls in the center of the table.

Dr. Canby always set the tone of the discussions, and yesterday, after the meeting, Marquand had remarked once again to himself on the skill with which the shrewd Chief Justice conducted the sessions. Arguments were kept to a minimum. By the time they got to the meetings, the judges had read six or seven books highly recommended by a panel of "first readers." These were known as "A" books, and each judge read every one of them. Certain other books, known as "B" books, were read by only two or three of the judges; some months, Marquand read three "B" books. The books were discussed over the lunch table, and those that any one of the judges did not like were disposed of first. Marquand had a tendency to become caustic during the meetings, and Dr. Canby was often on the verge of quieting him down when he was, as the Chief Justice sometimes put it, "too funny." Dr. Canby had no objection to levity, but he felt that an Associate Justice of the Book-of-the-Month Club should keep his humor within bounds. Marquand's humor ran to derision, especially of highly romantic costume novels filled with jolly, red-cheeked wholesome characters. "Why, they're all so goddam healthy it's positively painful!" he would cry, screwing up his face into an expression of complete disgust, scraping at his mustache with one hand and revolving the other hand in the air as though it were attached to a universal joint. Just the afternoon before, he and Fadiman, who had great respect for each other (Fadiman once said that Marquand was, in a sense, the Thackeray of his day), got into a furious argument over precisely such a novel — a huge English job, bristling with merry villagers, cute squires, and hustle-bustle plans for community gaiety. Marquand became rather violent in his denunciation of the chubby humor of this book, and Fadiman called him a misanthrope. Dr. Canby, who yielded to no man in his admiration for Marquand — he felt that he was in the tradition of Jane Austen and Trollope, and often spoke of "the beautiful patina of his work" — judiciously hurried along to another book, and Harry Scherman, who sat in during the meetings but had no vote, smiled obliquely.

Now Marquand looked at his watch and saw that he had twenty-five minutes to get to Grand

Central, where he was to meet Craig aboard the train. Marquand had never seen Craig, but he had talked with him on the phone a few days before, and he had felt that Craig sounded over-eager and tense. Marquand could sympathize. He knew some of the problems Craig faced in attempting to delineate another man's life, and he understood, as a result of his own days as a reporter on the Boston *Transcript* and, later as a writer for popular magazines, the rules and regulations under which topical writers like Craig had to operate. Standing now in his living room, he could not help feeling a certain sense of accomplishment and pride in his own work. He had managed to escape the pressure of the deadline, and the other rules and regulations. As a writer of novels, he was altogether his own master. It was a dangerous life, for if one did not follow a privately determined pattern of solid work, days and months and even years could pass without productivity. Marquand had solved that problem by severe self-discipline, and each morning while he was working on a novel, he and Miss Marjorie Davis, his secretary, started work at ten and kept at it until one-thirty or two, Marquand dictating and Miss Davis taking his words down on the typewriter. He enjoyed pacing the room, talking, revolving his hands, and occasionally glancing over Miss Davis's shoulder at what she was putting down. For years, he had struggled with the typewriter himself, but when he conceived the notion of writing *The Late George Apley,* he had experimented with dictating, and had found that it relaxed him and brought his thoughts to the surface of his mind with a minimum of pain. He had used that method with all his later books. In the morning, work; in the afternoon, reading and editing the typescript. Even when he was not writing a novel, he stuck closely to this schedule, and yesterday afternoon, after coming back uptown from the meeting, he had summoned Miss Davis and dictated a book review for the *Book-of-the-Month Club News,* and the paper he was to deliver before the Tuesday Night Club.

For an instant, at least, he was pleased with himself. *Melville Goodwin, USA* was selling beautifully. The dramatization of *Point of No Return* was a smash hit. Marquand suddenly glanced at Grant Wood's "Parson Weems' Fable," hanging over a sofa in the living room, and the second he did so, his sense of well-being disappeared. There you had it — one minute content, the next dissatisfied and troubled again. Adelaide had always wanted to own an original Grant Wood, and here it was, and it vaguely disturbed him. The picture distracted him and made it difficult to work, so he never looked in its direction while dictating. But it was a fine thing to own, even if a good many solid citizens considered it an unpatriotic picture. Stanley Resor, who was the head of J. Walter Thompson, the advertising agency in which Marquand worked briefly when he came home from France in 1918, had had an option on the picture but had dropped it after taking a look. He felt that Wood had been disrespectful to the fable of little George and the cherry tree. Perhaps he had. Wood had painted a small boy wearing knee breeches and holding a hatchet, but the face was that of an old man; in fact, it was the face of a Gilbert Stuart Washington. The picture was a parody of eighteenth-century art, and Parson Weems, standing slyly in one corner, holding back a curtain to reveal the scene, gave the impression of a person who was putting something over on someone. Wood had worked hard on the picture; it had taken him quite some time to finish it. Marquand knew that, and he admired the picture, and he was grateful that Wood had granted him, as a sort of professional courtesy, twenty-five per cent off on it, but nevertheless something about it distressed him.

Marquand's sense of having been jarred disappeared almost as swiftly as it had come when he walked across the silent room and caught sight of an old lacquer chest standing against the wall. On top of the chest there was a red cushion, and on top of the cushion resided a plump and satisfied-looking wooden Chinese goddess — the Goddess of Mercy, Kwan Yin. To the precise extent that "Parson Weems' Fable" jarred Marquand, the contented features of Kwan Yin, he found, gave him, even at the merest glance, a sensation of well-being. Indeed, looking at the figure of Kwan Yin now brought back to Marquand that overpowering sense of happiness that comes over one when one is travelling in far-off lands. God, thought Marquand, how I loved China when I was there, and how I wish I were taking a trip now — not to Germany (to hell with the Germans) and not to France (with the Gloire de France and all that gone now), or to sunny, romantic Italy, or to England (with its austerity), but perhaps into the Gobi to watch the nomadic Mongols out on the lonely plains building their little fires of dung. They make out, he thought, they make out somehow. They get along. And an Occidental mingling with them can get along, too, but one must be careful what one eats. God, he thought, to be watching them boiling their sheep! (One is safe with mutton, probably.) He would like to be hearing lamas blowing their horns, or see camels again, or, better still, go to the east coast of Africa and see people living in beehive huts. Or perhaps to Egypt, to the Mena House, out near the Pyramids. Not to Shepheard's, in Cairo, even if the place were still there; the last time, there were fleas in the chairs in the lobby. A glance at the Goddess of Mercy convinced him of the benefits to be derived from travel, and it reminded him, too, of something he had encountered in China that had left a deep impression.

For it was in China that he had met up with *fêng-shui*, a term that really means "wind and water" but that Marquand preferred to think of as describing "the balance of things." The Chinese still lived up to that when he was there in 1934 and 1935, when he met Adelaide, whom he subsequently married. He was staying, in 1935, at Mrs. Calhoun's Boarding House in Peiping, a remarkable hostel with a No. 1 boy and a courtyard, and he wore shorts and a pith helmet, and Adelaide Hooker and her sister Helen — the sister was en route from Japan to Ireland to marry Ernie O'Malley, the Irish Revolutionist (another sister, Blanchette, settled down with John D. Rockefeller III) — mistook him for an Englishman on, so to speak, the beach. But that was another story. *Fêng-shui* was on his mind. In China, *fêng-shui* was looked after by the soothsayers. Soothsayers have the final say when it comes to *fêng-shui,* and they exercise their authority in curious and helpful ways. One would not dream of putting up a new building or entering upon a new enterprise without consulting the soothsayer, who would tell one where to place the screen to ward off evil spirits — everything is all right as long as you face south, but if you plan to build facing north, a screen must be erected somewhere, and it is the soothsayer who knows where. Soothsayers might sit for fifteen or twenty minutes in deep concentration before making a pronouncement. Everything about the Orient had fascinated him, especially the street entertainers, such as the sword swallowers and the men with the dancing mice, but his most profound respect had been reserved for the soothsayers and their insight into *fêng-shui*, the balance of things.

He remembered one incident quite clearly. He was dining with a friend in Peiping when his friend abruptly clapped his hands for the No. 1 boy, who entered silently. "Send in the fortune-teller," his friend said, and a moment later a tall, elderly Chinese with a mandarin mustache came into the dining room and began to gaze at Marquand. For several minutes there was a portentous silence, and when he spoke, he spoke with a delicate softness of tone. Marquand's friend translated. "In China, there is no social classification for this man," said the fortune-teller, still gazing intently at Marquand. "He is not a student, but he is almost a student. He is quick-tempered and successful. Should he gain knowledge of the complexity of social relationships, he will live to be seventy." The soothsayer then backed away several feet and stared with terrifying intensity at Marquand. "Please," he said to Marquand's friend, "I implore this man to wear a mustache, even if it is a small one." He offered no explanation for this singular request other than a few vague but persuasive remarks about the need for restoring the balance to Marquand's face. A mustache, he evidently felt, would do the trick, would bring out the full quality of the face. Marquand was shaken by the experience. He promptly grew a mustache, and had retained it, and now, looking at the Goddess of Mercy, he felt that she and *fêng-shui* had dealt kindly with him and that he had done well to take the soothsayer's advice. He was fifty-eight, and in good health, and successful, and, more than most writers, he had achieved a certain balance of things.

Somewhere in the empty apartment, a clock struck the three-quarter note. Suddenly frenzied, Marquand went into the foyer, put on his Lock hat and his F. L. Dunne overcoat — splendid products of London and Boston, respectively — picked up the golf bag that he would drop off at the Myopia Club north of Boston on the way to Newburyport and the bright-brown leather suitcase he had packed the night before, and rang for the elevator, the door of which opened into his foyer. He waited a moment and rang again, impatiently. The elevator came, and the elderly operator, who wore a blue uniform and looked like an old League of Nations diplomat, bustled his bags into the car. Marquand was silent during the trip down. What one needs in life is a balance of things, he thought. But the minute you think you have it, there is some damn picture on a wall, and one glance and the balance is gone. On the ground floor, another elderly attendant, who resembled the elevator man and was similarly uniformed, carried his bags to the street. He set them down, blew his whistle for a cab, helped Marquand into it, and put the bags gently in at his feet. These fellows running elevators and tooting all day long for taxis have *fêng-shui* of a sort, too, but God spare me, thought Marquand. "Where to, Mister?" asked the cabdriver. There was a note of anger in his voice, as though he resented having to wait even five seconds for his instructions. Marquand took an instant dislike to the man. "Oh, I am terribly sorry," he said. "Grand Central, please, and hurry, if you will."

3

Traffic Gets Worse Every Year

MARQUAND settled back in the taxi, and
it headed west on Sixty-Seventh Street
and then swung south on Park Avenue
and down the broad and almost empty street. The
day was damp and windy, and fast-moving gray
clouds were sweeping over the city. Marquand
felt that he could detect, even in the cold, a hint
of spring, but the hint was reluctantly, forbid-
dingly given, as though spring were conflicting
meanly with winter and offering nothing better.
He checked over carefully in his mind what lay
ahead of him for the day. He would meet Craig
on the train. He held Seat 25 in Car 302 and
Craig held Seat 26. This would place Craig across
the aisle — a blessing, since it would obviate the
necessity of their turning those absurd parlor-car
chairs around to face each other, which would
mean getting their legs hopelessly entwined. The

old-time parlor-car seats, he reflected, did not re-
cline like barber chairs, and the old-time parlor cars
themselves were spared those public-address sys-
tems over which a brisk voice announced, "You
are now leaving Grand Central Station in New
York on the scenic shore route for Boston." Good
God, thought Marquand, if there is anybody
aboard one of those trains so stupid as not to
know he is leaving Grand Central on a train for
Boston, he doesn't deserve to be told. The taxi
stopped for a red light at the corner of Fifty-
Eighth Street. Once on the train, thought Marquand, Craig will talk most of the way to Boston
— almost five hours of talk, and questions, and
answers. But I can avoid some of it by reading.
I can read the *Times*, and smoke a pipe in the
club car, and read the short story in the *News,*
and go over some work for the Book-of-the-Month.
This will kill some time. Once in Boston, I'll
show Craig some of the sights, and take him to
lunch, perhaps at the Somerset Club or the Tavern — it will be a treat for him — and then we'll
ride on to Newburyport, and Craig can see the
place at Kent's Island, and then supper at L. P.
Dodge's, and then the paper before the Tuesday
Night Club. All things considered, a dreadful
day, and yet one that may be filled with certain
compensations, since it is always flattering to be

the center of attention, and later to be surrounded
by old friends who have enjoyed, or pretended to
enjoy, one's paper.

Marquand could now see the clock on the
Grand Central Building. He had only eight minutes to reach the station. That was New York for
you. You were lucky to make a train these days.
You were lucky, perhaps, to stay alive at all amid
the constant rushing and the ceaseless tensions.
Traffic was piling up ahead now, and horns were
blowing, and Marquand found that he was puzzled by himself. It was difficult for him to understand why he had come north so soon from Treasure Island, the place he rented in the Bahamas.
The spot was heaven-sent — a narrow little strip
of coral limestone rock, three and a half miles
from end to end and not more than a quarter of
a mile wide at the widest point, four miles from
Nassau. Marquand went down there in the early
winter, with Adelaide and the three little children
and Miss Davis, and it was a life of nearly unbe-
lievable forgetfulness and relaxation, at least at
those times when one wanted to forget and relax.
He could not conceive of a man's renting such a
spot and then returning to New York before the
winter was over, but he had become restless, and
here he was now, sitting in a taxi, late for the
eight-o'clock train to Boston. Marquand had

spent two winters on Treasure Island, and it was
an almost perfect place to work and play. The
island, originally called Salt Cay, had an old, and
even dishonorable, history, having been used in
the early days as a hiding place for pirates, who
holed up there while their chief sailed over to
Nassau to blackmail the British and collect their
gold pieces. Once, it had been a coconut planta-
tion, but today there was little foliage other than
a few palm trees and some Australian pine. The
late John McCutcheon, the Chicago *Tribune* car-
toonist, had bought the island in 1916 and re-
named it Treasure Island. Near the lagoon —
many of those funny little islands in the Bahamas
have lagoons, and only the most experienced boat-
men can navigate them — McCutcheon had built
a stone tower, which still stood. Treasure Island
was the sort of place where Marquand had always
dreamed of living — an expression of the novelist's desire to live out his poor span in properly
dreamlike fashion. It was the sort of place that,
God forbid, Maugham might settle into. Marquand did not have an especially high regard for
Maugham, but he would concede that Treasure
Island was a Maugham-type island, with what
seemed like dozens of black servants overrunning
the place and doing one's bidding with a cryptic
smile. The buildings were crude but comfortable

— the main house, yellow, built like a Malayan planter's house, with shutters and a red roof and a broad veranda facing on the lagoon; two small guesthouses, thirty yards away, hard by the portable canvas house in which Miss Davis and he worked in the mornings. The termites had partially taken over the place, and the buildings were falling down, but it had an exquisite charm by day, when he and his guests, followed by the ubiquitous banana quits, picked up shells or watched the sea and the sky, and an added charm by night, when the kerosene lamps were lighted. Time stood still on Treasure Island, and here he was with only five minutes to spare, and just passing the Waldorf-Astoria. The evenings were perhaps the best times, he thought, when he and Adelaide would assemble in the big room in the big house with their guests — Lillian Gish, perhaps, or Secretary and Mrs. Lovett, or Mrs. Philip Barry, or the Lindberghs, or good old Dr. Canby — to listen to Josephas sing.

Josephas had been around the place for years, a courtly Negro, as much a part of the island as Captain Wilfred Sweeting, also a Negro, who could bring the motor sloop, the *Guanahani* — an old Caribbean name for a Bahama island — in through the lagoon in all but the very worst weather. They would gather to hear Josephas

strum on a guitar and solemnly sing the theme
song of the island, a faintly disturbing song di-
rected each night at a different guest:

> Too late, Mr. ——,
> But never mind,
> All your trials soon will be over.
> You go east and I go west.
> I will meet you in the buryin' ground.
> Your trials soon will be over.

Josephas had many other songs, including one
— a closing song — that contained the words "Lay
down, everybody, lay down and take your rest,"
and one dedicated, calypso-style, to Mrs. Marquand, and aimed at keeping her from making
too many trips to Nassau and bringing back too
many guests for lunch. The song had infinite
choruses, one of which went:

> Madam, madam,
> Don't go to Bay Street no mo'.
> No movie stars, no diplomats,
> No bankers in Jamaica hats.
> Madam, madam,
> Don't go to Bay Street no mo'.

Some nights, Josephas would stare at Marquand
and, strumming away, sing with great earnestness,
"O Lord, keep the boss in the center of Thy will,"

a song that always deeply affected Marquand. Other nights, the guests would troop to the water's edge to watch the strange, great hermit crabs. They would turn their flashlights on the creatures, which would scatter every which way.

But in spite of the temptation to lie about, Marquand always did a daily stint of good, hard work at Treasure Island, rising at the break of day, taking a quick dip in the ocean, and dictating to Miss Davis until noon. Then a drink or two, and lunch and conversation with the guests, and after that an afternoon of going over the work done in the morning. That was one thing he had taught himself — self-discipline, as a prerequisite of getting anything, anything at all, written, and he recalled now, as the taxi careened west on Forty-Seventh Street toward Vanderbilt Avenue (he had three minutes in which to make the train), something Sinclair Lewis had said to a class in writing at one of the universities. Marquand had been told of the incident. The room was filled to overflowing when Lewis stood up before the group. "How many of you here want to write?" he asked. All present raised their hands. "Then why in the hell aren't you home writing?" shouted Lewis, and sat down. Marquand had liked Red Lewis, but his tongue had been somewhat frightening. For the most part, though, he avoided being in the company of writers. They were too tense and jealous and morbid, and he made no attempt to move in their peculiar circles. Hemingway he had never met, or Faulkner; he regretted never having talked with Sherwood Anderson. Few writers ever came to Treasure Island, and if many had come, their talk, he was certain, would have driven him mad — especially the incessant din they would have set up about James, Fitzgerald, and Joyce. He suddenly thought back to that day in Taormina, in the twenties, when a friend introduced him, in the lobby of his hotel, to a strange creature in sandals, with red hair, and sockets for eyes, whose name he didn't catch. They chatted for a while about Sicily, and the man said that he was living somewhere in the hills. The next day, Marquand's friend asked him what he had thought of the odd-looking chap, and Marquand said, "He is quite off his trolley. Who is he?" "That was D.H. Lawrence," his friend said. His friend later asked Lawrence what *he* thought of Marquand, and Lawrence said, "The fellow is quite mad."

No, relationships with writers were difficult to endure, and he preferred the company of men like George W. Merck, his old classmate at Harvard, who was now president of the Merck chemical company. Merck was a huge man, and he was filled with huge ideas. He could be quite efficient and directorial when he came to the island.

Within fifteen minutes after turning up, he would have outlined a complete plan for enlarging everything on the place, for opening up the lagoon entrance to make it navigable at all times, and for transforming the salt water into drinking water. Marquand was amused by the plans, and by good old George for thinking them up — sanitation was a problem on the island, all right — just as he was alternately amused and dismayed by the attitude of almost everyone making his first visit to the place. When you came right down to it, the visitors were all grist to his mill. The questions they asked followed a routine. First they asked, "How is the plumbing here?" Then they asked, "Is there a telephone?" And then they usually remarked, sighing in the way non-writers usually sigh in the presence of a writer, "Just like Robert Louis Stevenson!" Robert Louis Stevenson my hat, thought Marquand. But the customs of the place were compelling, and he wished that he were drifting off to bed there now, with Josephas singing to the group, "Lay down, everybody, lay down and take your rest. Lay your head upon your Saviour's breast." The cab stopped at the Vanderbilt entrance to the terminal. He had one minute to catch the train, and there was no sign of a redcap. There never was a redcap when you needed one.

4

Trains May Be Slow, but They Get You There

CRAIG and Marquand maintained, for the most part, an odd silence during their ride together from New York to Boston. Craig had taken his seat, No. 26 in parlor car No. 302, at three minutes to eight. He had been convinced, when he glanced across the aisle at seat No. 25, which was empty, that Marquand would miss the train. The thought that he might not, after all, have the opportunity of accompanying Marquand to Boston and Newburyport brought beads of perspiration to Craig's forehead. In their way, the three minutes Craig had to wait for Marquand to arrive were a minor nightmare. But Marquand arrived a few seconds before the train pulled out. He was in a fury. He had been certain that the train would pull out without him, but suddenly a redcap had come along, and now, safe in Seat 25, he regretted that he had. The redcap had demanded the usual twenty-five cents for his suitcase and twenty-five for his golf bag. Marquand had always considered this price too steep — it was not as though the redcap himself kept much of the money — and, running up against it again this morning, he was so enraged that he was incapable of more than a nod to Craig until several minutes after the train had started.

"Well, sir," said Craig as the train emerged from the tunnel under Park Avenue, "here we are."

Marquand was conscious of having perceptibly winced, and he hoped that Craig had not noticed. There was no point in hurting the poor fellow's feelings — and, moreover, here they *were*.

"Do you mind if I ask you a few questions, just to get the ball rolling?" Craig said.

"Not at all," said Marquand.

"Well, sir," said Craig, "I always believe in first things first." He laughed nervously. "What better way to get the ball rolling than to ask where you were born? Where in New England, I mean."

"As a matter of fact," said Marquand, "I was born in Wilmington, Delaware."

"Well, I'll be damned," Craig said. "Wilmington, Delaware. Not New England, eh?"

"I beg your pardon?" said Marquand.

Craig indulged in another of his nervous laughs. "Well, you know how it is," he said. "John P. Marquand is celebrated as a New England writer. It's a part of the country he understands — he gets under its skin, you might say — and then it turns out that he was born in Wilmington, Delaware."

"I'm terribly sorry," said Marquand.

Craig appeared not to have heard. He was jotting down some notes in a small brown book he had taken from the inside pocket of his jacket. "Well," he said, "we're over the first hurdle. Did you ever go to school in Wilmington?"

"No," said Marquand. "I only lived there for a year or two."

"Oh, I see," said Craig, writing something else down in his book.

"I wonder very much," said Marquand, "if we could talk a little bit later on. I haven't had time to read the paper yet."

"That makes sense," said Craig. "Anyway, it's better to thaw out, and I haven't read the Alsops this morning. They usually hit the situation right on the nose."

Marquand smiled wanly and swung his chair around until it faced the window. He had brought a copy of the *Times* along, and he held it up before his face, but he did not read it.

Craig's simple question, "Where were you born?" had turned Marquand's thoughts in the direction of his parents and his childhood. Now, in the swiftly moving train to Boston, he found himself thinking of his father, Philip Marquand. Philip Marquand, still a charming and twinkly gentleman, though in his eighties, was becoming increasingly forgetful. He was living quietly in Concord, Massachusetts. Marquand visited him from time to time, and on each occasion the old gentleman greeted him in the same fashion. He said, inevitably, "John, where is the money?" Not long ago, Marquand had visited him on a bleak New England day. A heavy snow was falling. Having asked where the money was, Philip Marquand suddenly said, "John, it's time for spring planting. Let's get out of here," and John took him over to a window and showed him the white countryside and the ever mounting drifts of snow. Philip Marquand stood for a moment looking out upon the scene, and then turned to his son. "By God, John," he said, "you're right!" There was no getting away from the fact that he had been something of a trial to John, and to John's mother, who died in 1932. "Where is the money?" The very thought of the question brought a deep tinge of pink to Marquand's face. Where is the money indeed! John and his mother had never

quite known where the money went. Marquand
remembered now, with a tempered bitterness, that
he had, while he was a successful *Saturday Evening Post* writer, commanding the highest rates,
established his father in a small business in Newburyport, raising Rhode Island Reds. They were
the finest Rhode Island Reds in New England
and the eggs they laid brought in a tidy sum. But
no one ever quite knew what Philip Marquand
did with his money. One morning, he received a
fifteen-hundred-dollar check in payment for a big
shipment of chicks, put on his best hat and coat,
selected his favorite walking stick, and announced, with a strange smile, that he intended
to spend the day in Boston. He was a short, trim
man — he had been the featherweight sparring
champion of his class, '89, at Harvard — and he
cut an elegant figure as he left for the railroad station, jauntily swinging his cane. Nothing was
heard from him for two days. He returned, de-
jected, on the second evening. The smile was
gone from his face and the swagger from his walk.
The fifteen hundred dollars was gone, too. Marquand asked what had happened to the money.
"I blew it in, and it's none of your damned business," Philip Marquand said.

That was the way it had always been, Marquand remembered. Philip Marquand had al-

ways been a gambler; even if he won, he ulti-
mately lost, since he would toss his winnings into
one grand plunge. This time I will make a kill-
ing, he would say, playing a stock-market hunch,
and the money would be gone. John, his only
child, had lived his entire life in dread of gambling and the gambling habit. In fact, he often
wished that the psychologists — though he did
not have any special confidence in them — would
investigate the roots of gambling and the motives
of gamblers. They might discover a great many
things that would spare families distress. Philip
Marquand's talent for dropping whatever funds
he possessed into a seemingly bottomless pit had
been a governing influence in the life of his son,
and had kept the boy's family pretty much on the
move during what writers like to call "the forma-
tive years." There had been Marquands in Newburyport since old Daniel Marquand left the Isle
of Guernsey, in 1732, and settled in the small sea-
port town thirty-two miles northeast of Boston.
Joseph, Daniel's son, had been a noted and ex-
tremely successful owner of privateer vessels during the American Revolution; he grew so wealthy
that he became embarrassed about it, and would
pray, "Lord, stay Thy hand, Thy servant hath
enough." The Lord conceivably heard the cry,
for Joseph lost his money. John's grandfather

had been a solvent banker, and when he died, in 1900, he left to be divided among his six children, including John's father, an estate in the neighborhood of half a million dollars. John's mother, a Fuller, came from splendid New England stock, and was, in fact, not only the niece but the namesake of the feminist and Transcendentalist Margaret Fuller. By the time John was born, in 1893, Philip Marquand, a Phi Beta Kappa at Harvard and a graduate of M.I.T., had left New England and taken a job as a civil engineer with the American Bridge Company in Wilmington. In fact, that had been the cause of John's being born in Wilmington, Delaware, and not in the snowbound hills of grim old New England, as the absurd figure across the aisle had so innocently assumed. Soon after John's birth, the family suddenly moved to Newburyport, and then to Pinckney Street, in Boston, and then to Concord. Philip Marquand's father subsequently established him in the bond business, and when John was a lad of six or seven, the family moved to New York, to 51 East Thirtieth Street. He and a nurse would go to frolic with a large hoop in Madison Square park, and look into the windows of the old F. A. O. Schwarz toy store nearby. For a while, matters went well with Philip Marquand. His bond business prospered, and the family moved again, this time to Rye. Looking out the window of the train, Marquand was struck by the curiously fictional circumstances of life, for the train was at that very moment hurtling past the Rye station.

In his mind's eye, Marquand could see again their old house, which stood directly on the Post Road, and the barn behind the house, and the old horse called Prince, who, hitched to the carriage and driven by a coachman, took his father each morning to the Rye station, the same station they had just passed. His father lived elegantly, and although there were few cars on the roads in those days, Philip Marquand owned one — an Orient Buckboard, a formidable two-passenger vehicle with the motor behind the seat. Every once in a while, on a Sunday, they would drive together to the American Yacht Club, on the Sound. On Sundays, too, there were races on the Post Road, when the drivers of horseless carriages would find out how far they could go on one gallon of gasoline. The panic of 1907 wiped his father out and, John was convinced, changed the course of his own life. "I was just a well-bred little boy living comfortably with my parents," he often told Adelaide while recounting some of the vicissitudes of his life, "and the rug was pulled out from under me." He was fifteen when his father found himself in serious financial difficulties.

Philip Marquand fell back upon his engineering skill again and got jobs in Los Angeles and San Francisco. Marquand's mother took the boy up to Newburyport and left him in the care of her husband's two maiden sisters, Bessie and Molly, at the old family homestead, Curzon's Mill, several miles out of town. She then joined her husband in California. The boy attended Newburyport High School, and came under the influence of his two aunts and a great-aunt, Aunt Mary Curzon, who, at eighty-five, played dominoes or backgammon every evening, read aloud from Pepys' Diary for three hours before retiring, and whose most frequent conversational topic was the Fire. The Fire had occurred in 1811, and had destroyed not only the wharf and house of her Grandfather Marquand but his three-hundred-ton brig, the *George Washington,* which had been docked alongside the wharf. The Fire, in the eyes of Aunt Mary, was the most villainous and decisive act in American history — of considerably more importance than such minor incidents as the Civil War.

Marquand's life with his maiden aunts was severely restricted. He always had to be well brushed and combed, and well behaved. There was little chance for shouting or the horseplay of youth. His aunts were all avid readers, and Aunt

Bessie read him every play of Shakespeare's. The classics and the Bible were in constant use at the Mill, and to this day Marquand could recite an astonishing number of passages from the Good Book, and he knew Scott's Waverley Novels pretty much by heart. He missed the old days of swimming and tennis at the American Yacht Club, and he missed, too, the promise and security he had come to expect in his life. Looking back now, though, he felt that his having attended Newburyport High, instead of some such place as Groton, St. Mark's, or St. Paul's (the type of school he would normally have been sent to), had had a healthy effect upon him as a writer, for it had introduced him to something or somebody other than the way of life and the crowd he might have fallen in with. His father soon found himself in Panama, where he became a sort of supervisor at the canal they were building down there, and in 1914 went back to Wilmington, this time as a designing engineer with the Edge Moor Iron Works. John's mother faithfully accompanied her husband on these journeys, and he could still feel her pain at the unsettled conditions of her life, so unfamiliar, so unlike the quiet Cambridge of her birth. In 1929, his mother came into a small sum of money. John immediately persuaded her to place this in trust for herself and her

husband. Philip Marquand was hurt and humili-
ated. He meant well; he was sure that if he had
invested the money wisely and nurtured it — it
was just a matter of being shrewd and outsmart-
ing the market — he could have doubled or
tripled it. He paced the floor on many occasions,
many years later, crying out, "If only you hadn't
put that money of your mother's in trust!"

5

You're Only Young Once

MARQUAND became aware that someone was tapping him on the shoulder.
It was Craig; he had his notebook in his
hand, and his face bore an eager expression. He
seemed poised to deliver a few more of his penetrating questions. "I was wondering about education," he said. "You went to Harvard, of course.
And the class?"

"Fifteen," said Marquand.

"Oh, I see," said Craig. "And did you have a
good time there?"

"Not especially," said Marquand.

"Oh, I see," said Craig.

You don't see at all, thought Marquand. How
could you possibly see? In fact, how could anyone see, including perhaps himself, since the bit-
ter was so closely connected with the sweet? Harvard was for him in many ways a lonely place,
partly because of his natural shyness and reserve,

and partly because of his postion in life. He had
very little money to spend, and as a consequence,
although he always wore an overcoat of great
warmth and splendor, and smoked the best to-
bacco, he did not mingle with the gay young
blades of the Harvard social clubs, such as the
Fly and the Porcellian. He was a member of no
club, a fact that, if he thought about it at all, he
attributed to his having come to Harvard from
Newburyport High rather than from one of the
numerous prep schools from which graduates
poured into Harvard freshman classes, as from a
cornucopia. Marquand lived quietly in a boarding house at 7 Linden Street, in Cambridge, and
had a parrot who could say "Hello, boys." Before
settling down to the routine of liberal arts, he
studied metallurgy and chemistry, and achieved
local laboratory fame for his ability, in Chemistry III, to operate a blowpipe, with which
he could make qualitative analyses much more
rapidly than by ordinary laboratory methods. His
interest in chemistry threw him into a reserved
friendship with another shy undergraduate student, James Bryant Conant, who also lived at 7
Linden. A favorite sport of the residents of 7
Linden, and one in which Marquand occasionally participated, was the Two-Drink Dash, which
consisted of the young men's leaving their rooms
in 7 Linden at staggered times during an evening,

travelling by subway to the Holland Wine Company, a bar on Essex Street, in Boston, drinking down two fast ones, and returning to 7 Linden, the winner being the one who made the round trip the fastest. At the time, the Two-Drink Dash had seemed like an adventure of the first magnitude, such as crossing the English Channel by plane, but now it seemed to Marquand, as he looked back, a bit foolish. Still, there *had* been a challenge in the Two-Drink Dash, and problems to work out, and with the intensity of youth they spent hours debating the proper method of reaching the Holland Wine Company. Some believed that the wisest course was to travel to Boylston Street by subway, which entailed changing trains at Park Street, while others — and, perhaps, Marquand felt, the wisest ones — emerged from the underground at the Park Street station and ran along the Common to Essex Street. Sometimes the journey was in vain; one day he made it to the Holland Wine Company in excellent time and then, to his shame, was refused a drink by the bartender, who said, with a maddening air of authority, "Run along, sonny. You look too young."

But the Two-Drink Dash was merely an ephemeral charade in what had been for the most part a lonely period for Marquand. He kept his own counsel and made only a few intimate friends, and his classmates often wondered why they

would see nothing of him for weeks at a time.
They conjectured about the cause of these dis-
appearances, and concluded that he either was
studying hard, had run out of funds and did not
feel like facing his companions, or led a dark,
mysterious life of his own. Marquand's social life
while an undergraduate was on the whole fairly
painful, and it was not until many years later,
after he had graduated from the hallowed Yard,
that he could bear even to think about the celebrated dances at the Somerset Hotel, which everybody who was anybody attended, resplendent in
white tie and tails. The dances were invariably
preceded by teas, and all the nice little under-
graduates were invited to one or another of the
teas, at somebody or other's home. Once Marquand accepted an invitation to a tea at a house
on Commonwealth Avenue, in Boston. He could
still recall the agony of his entrance into the
crowded drawing room, alive with knots of con-
versationalists and friendly chatter. Marquand
reached a point against one wall and stayed there
for half an hour, during which time he spoke to
no one and no one spoke to him. The acid of this
discomfiture had etched itself deep in his memory.
Not until some thirty years later, when memory
had been overlaid by life, did he come to view
the experience in some sort of perspective. He
could then look upon it with a certain mature

tolerance, for he no longer had that same feeling of being alone and unwanted. He was now a member of the Somerset Club and the Tavern Club, a respected author, even a chronicler of the ways and mores of Boston itself. He realized that his painful experience on Commonwealth Avenue had not been the result of a deliberate snub. It had been a perfectly normal occurrence. Everyone in that room, he now told himself, had known everyone else, and they had all assumed, without so much as even assuming it, that he knew everyone, too. That, in a sense, was Boston.

At Harvard, Marquand avoided participating in manifestations of college spirit; the notion of hail-hail-hail and die-for-dear-old-Harvard did not appeal to him. Athletic rallies struck him as juvenile, and he soon developed, as he put it years later, "a spirit of indifference." He kept a sharp eye out for the type known as the Big Man on Campus, and this vigilance served a useful purpose when he began writing novels because he had built up a storehouse of experience on which to draw for some of his most entertaining characters — most notably Bo-jo Brown, a booster of monumental proportions, who was satirized in *H. M. Pulham, Esquire*. Marquand's small circle of devoted friends were not only enormously impressed by his intelligence but were enormously amused by his ability to mimic everything and

everybody in the Harvard world, but many years
after his graduation, and after he had made his
mark in the literary world, he was constantly running into members of his class he had never so
much as said hello to during his undergraduate
days, and they almost invariably claimed'to have
had a warm friendship with him "back at Cambridge." Marquand never could figure out why
such encounters always secretly delighted him,
and he now recalled that while passing through
Hawaii during World War II, he happened upon
one of the Harvard greats, a former celebrated
backfield runner. When Marquand was at Harvard, this man, although he had nodded to him
occasionally and had once called him by his first
name, had moved in an orbit several million
light-years away from that of Marquand's, but in
Hawaii the football player, who was doing war-
time duty in the Islands, said, "Hello, Johnny!
Do you remember the time I picked you out of
the gutter at the Woodcock?" The Woodcock was
a Boston dine-and-dance establishment of the
period, where the sportier members of the Harvard undergraduate body went to meet scarlet
women. Marquand had never set foot in the place,
but he discovered that he was flattered by the
man's story, and he could not bring himself to
disabuse him of it. On the other hand, even
though he met each year with a group of fifty

or more of his classmates who called themselves
the June Brides and congregated at the Essex
County Club, on the North Shore, in Manchester,
he found the activities of alumni and alumni
groups a phase of life almost entirely worth ridi-
culing.

He and other old Harvards often remarked
upon the loneliness of their lives at Harvard and
the feeling of insularity that had affected those
who were unwilling to throw in their lot with the
herd. One night, many years after all three of
them had graduated, he met up somewhere with
Archie Roosevelt, one of Teddy's sons, and Robert Nathan, the writer, and the talk turned, as it
so frequently did among Harvard men, to Harvard. Nathan remarked sadly that he hadn't
known anyone at Harvard, that he had always
crossed to the other side of the street when one of
the big wheels came along, and that no one had
had anything to do with him, because he was
Jewish. Now that he was a successful writer, he
said, he was appealed to continually to make a
speech or produce some literary contribution to
some alumni publication. Marquand smiled
wryly and said that the experience was not
unique. He, he said, did not even have the ex-
cuse of being Jewish. "My situation was much
worse than yours," he went on. "They would ask
where I had gone to school, and I would tell them

Newburyport High, and a look of horror would pass over their faces. Now I get nothing but letters from classmates addressed 'Dear old Johnny' and asking me to do such and such." Archie Roosevelt smiled broadly. "You fellows had it easy," he said. "Look at my situation. I was the son of a former President of the United States, perhaps the most famous figure of his time. I had gone to Groton. Do you think anyone paid any attention to me? I never made the Porcellian."

Marquand glanced at his watch and realized that the train would soon be in New Haven, and it occurred to him that although he might not have had a roaring good time at Harvard, he had undoubtedly made out better than if he had gone to Yale. He once had had a Harvard character alight from a Boston train for a cigarette and a stretch on the New Haven platform, and the very thought of New Haven and of being there had made the character shudder. No, Harvard had not been all loneliness and hard work. There were, after all, the days on the *Lampoon*. Candidates turned up each Wednesday evening in the Candidates' Room and submitted their stuff; two pages of a scrapbook had to be filled with their published work before they could become members of the editorial board. The initiation was a ceremony he would never forget. He was ordered to stand in a window of the *Lampoon* offices and cry out, at the top of his voice, "FIRE! FIRE! FIRE! RAPE! RAPE! RAPE! Don't shoot! I'll marry the girl! My name is John P. Marquand." Not long before, Marquand had gone over some back numbers of the *Lampoon* of his period, and he had to confess that the humor in them completely escaped him. He had the feeling that he was reading something in code. He almost wished he had not looked into the matter, for he had run across such jokes as:

> FIRST MAN: "Are you going to the garbage man's ball tonight?"
> SECOND MAN: "No, I rather think it beyond the pale."

And yet, looking at the old numbers had brought back some of the good times, such as the *Lampoon* dinners, and the sense of superiority that came over a young man once he was a staff member and in a position to judge the contributions of those seeking a place on the staff.

The train stopped at New Haven for several minutes to change engines, and Marquand and Craig stepped out onto the platform for a smoke.

"After your formal education was completed at Harvard," Craig asked, once again taking out his notebook, "what did you do?"

Marquand felt for a moment as though he were about to wince again. "I went to work on the

Boston *Transcript*," he said politely, and Craig set down the fact in his notebook.

"The *old* Boston *Transcript?*" asked Craig.

"The very same one," said Marquand as the conductor mercifully cried "All aboard!"

"Working on the *Transcript* must have been an experience," Craig said, after they had settled down again in their seats.

"It was an experience, all right," said Marquand, pulling a set of galley proofs from his briefcase. He pretended to read them, and out of the corner of his eye he could see that Craig was daydreaming and not too anxious to pursue his questioning.

The *Transcript*. Marquand had not really thought of the *Transcript* for years. He could recall that his father helped him get the job there; the managing editor, George S. Mandell, had been a classmate of Philip Marquand's. The old *Transcript's* offices were at the corner of Washington and Milk Streets; they were pretty dusty, and the place had about it an air of tradition. Now the *Transcript*, like so many other things of one's youth, was gone, and, thinking of its demise, Marquand remembered the remark that used to be made to young fellows who were trying to get on its staff. "You may not get paid much," people would say, "but the *Transcript* will take care of you in your old age." One morning, the

Transcript just rolled over and sank noiselessly, like a tired old vessel in a distant, lonely sea. In Marquand's time, the *Transcript* paid new reporters fifteen dollars a week. He lived on his salary for a year, taking quarters in a rooming house for two dollars and fifty cents a week. The *Transcript* management permitted itself a few minor charitable indulgences; on Election Night, when everybody hung around the office awaiting the returns, all hands were served a free meal, and on Thanksgiving Day each and every member of the staff was entitled to a free turkey, which was to be picked up at the Faneuil Hall market nearby. Marquand had to admit that he showed no special aptitude as a reporter. He covered an Orangemen's parade and some sort of strike, and he went around to see how the war then raging in Europe had affected Boston charities. He found that it had not affected Boston charities to any dramatic extent. The city editor was on the verge of letting him out when, thanks to a sudden opening, Marquand tried out for and landed a job as an assistant to Burton Kline, the *Transcript* magazine editor, whose section was published as part of each Wednesday's and Saturday's paper. He was made school-and-college editor; in addition, he clipped items of interest from the British papers.

The *Transcript* was a maze of feature departments; there was an automobile editor, a column of jokes called "Facts and Fancies," a women's-club editor, and a department called "Churchmen Afield." Marquand had enjoyed himself in a mild way; he knew everybody on the staff and everybody knew him. The *Transcript* was, in a sense, a family. H. T. Parker, the famous drama critic, whose perceptive reviews were always signed "H.T.P.," took a liking to the young man and often invited him to go along to openings. Boston was a great theatre town in those days; the Hollis was operating, and the Boston and the Plymouth and the New Wilbur; and, for musicals, the Colonial; and Keith's, for vaudeville, a form of entertainment Marquand despised, even though he occasionally reviewed the Keith's bill. He and Parker would eat a sedate dinner and head for the theatre. "Don't talk to me between the acts," H.T.P. always said. "I don't want my opinion prejudiced." And Marquand scrupulously obeyed the injunction. Old H.T.P. There was a character. We don't have that kind any more, Marquand mused; why, he always wrote with a pencil, and he had a cubicle off the editorial room, from which he would emerge from time to time, shouting, for all the editorial room to hear, "I will not be disturbed! I will not be disturbed!" There was no getting away from it, the *Transcript* had provided an enriching, if circumscribed, experience.

6

C'est la Guerre

THE world itself was pressing in on Marquand, as it was on all the young men of his generation, and although he was never one to shed public crocodile tears in later years over what some writers called "the lost generation" — the very term nauseated him — he was to be swept up in the contemporary currents as much as any man. Marquand was a member of Battery A of the First Massachusetts Artillery, and just prior to America's entrance into the war he obtained leave from the *Transcript* and went with his battery, by day coach, to Fort Bliss, outside El Paso, on the Mexican border, where he stayed from July to September, 1916. He was a private and a cannoneer, and he shared a tent with good old Bruce Lancaster; also, good old Gordon Hammersley was in his section. Marquand never did a blessed thing at Fort Bliss but clean up manure, and he did not take too kindly to Army life, but it added a layer of experience to what had gone before, and he did enjoy the reception the battery received when it returned to Boston and, accompanied by local ice-wagon horses, marched through the streets past cheering crowds.

When the United States entered the war, in April, 1917 — there were high hopes that once the Hun was defeated, the world would see a new era of progress — Marquand went to Officers' Training Camp at Plattsburg. Plattsburg was filled with fine men. Thomas Jefferson Coolidge was there. The Yale contingent was there, too — Morris Hadley, Kenneth Simpson, and the rest. Marquand found Plattsburg terrifying — he was a young man who had no great inclination toward barracks life — but he did well. He could not permit himself to do less. One misstep at the camp and he would be shipped home before his three months were up — an inconceivable humiliation. For if one were sent home, what would one say? When he left Plattsburg, as a first lieutenant, he went to Camp Devens, and from there to First Army Headquarters Regiment at Fort Greene, in Charlotte, North Carolina. He could speak and write French, and the authorities felt that he would be of great use on the other side, doing a sort of military-police job when the troops disembarked in France — handling various questions of a *parlez-vous* nature. He was about to go over with a motley group, which included a good many New York policemen, some society boys, and an assortment of Canucks and Creoles, when he was transferred — this was the Army — to the Fourth Division, Artillery Brigade Headquarters. When they got to France, they were promptly shipped to an artillery school outside Bordeaux, where Marquand became proficient in artillery orientation. The instructor was one of those men one never forgets. He was a battle-scarred Frenchman, a veteran of many French colonial struggles, and he was the proud possessor of a gold jaw, a silver skull, and a wooden leg. This grizzled warrior liked Marquand immensely, and when the group was getting ready to move up to the front, he issued orders for Marquand to stay behind and become an artillery instructor. The carnage at Château-Thierry was about to begin, and Marquand felt the need to get into action. He protested the order. The old Frenchman was incredulous. Such enthusiasm struck him as ridiculous. "I cannot understand, *mon fils*," he told Marquand. "I simply cannot understand why, after you have looked at me, with my gold jaw, my silver skull, and my wooden leg, you should still wish to get into action. You can stay here in Bordeaux, teach, and have wine, women, and pleasure. *Quelle folie!"*

Marquand preferred to forget his experiences in the war. Even now, seated in the weather-controlled comfort of the parlor car, decades after the event, he preferred to forget the war; he was not one to recount his battle experiences. He fought bravely and well from July, 1918, to the end of October, much of the time with the 77th Regiment Field Artillery, in the bloody business of the Vesle River and at St. Mihiel and in the Argonne, and the war was to him, in retrospect, a great deal of noise, and many guns going off, and masses of dead, and thousands upon thousands of tired men. He had no big memories of the war, since he had pushed it deep inside his mind, and only the most inconsequential incidents remained near the surface. He could recall — and in recalling wondered why he recalled — passing through a village on the way to Château-Thierry and watching a group of soldiers scrambling madly in a yard for a mess of old French coins from the days of Louis XVIII and Charles X. The coins had been placed in a well for safekeeping. A shell had burst nearby and sent the coins flying, and the men were scrambling for them. That was the vignette of the war that stayed with him, and he attached to it no special significance. Perhaps the wild scrambling of the men had some deeper meaning for him, but he was not aware what it could be, and he rather doubted whether it meant anything more than that a tired group of bored, slogging men had found a momentary diversion. One tried to forget the bloodshed, even as one tried to forget the bloodshed of World War II. He tried not to think of the morning at Iwo Jima — the morning of the landings, as the perfectly timed invasion got under way. He had gone out there as a correspondent for a magazine, and he watched the attack from the bridge of the *Nevada*. The efficiency and the machinelike quality of the military operation held him spellbound. The *Nevada* went as close to the beach as possible and fought it out with Japanese shore batteries. The air was filled with phosphorus and flame, and the LCI's went toward the shore, paralleled the shore, and were about to shoot when the Japs let loose. One of the small boats came back along-side the *Nevada*, her scuppers running with blood. And yet even amidst the coldly calculated horror of the invasion, he saw, as he could still see most vividly — he was on the bridge with the captain and the admiral — a Filipino mess boy bringing up some coffee and sandwiches just as one of the *Nevada's* big guns went off. The mess boy was lifted off the floor and the dishes were lifted off the tray, and then the sandwiches and coffee were back on the tray, and the mess boy had his feet on the floor again and was serving the admiral and the captain as though nothing had happened.

Marquand passed through Paris a few days before the armistice in November, 1918, but he engaged in none of the hinky-dinky and ooh-la-la revelry that so many veterans of the first war lovingly recall. He certainly did not feel like a hero, and there was nothing to celebrate then. He stayed in Paris forty-eight hours. The military police objected to the pants he was wearing. They hauled him in, and he told them the pants were regulation. "The trouble with you is you've been behind the lines too long," he said. Furthermore, he suggested that if they didn't like the pants he was wearing, they could damn well find him another pair. They were impressed and let him go.

Once back in the States, Marquand did what thousands upon thousands of other men were doing. He went to visit his parents briefly — they were still in Wilmington — and he looked around for a job in New York. There was no great difficulty finding work. Kline, his old Boston editor, was now at the *Tribune*, working on the magazine section. F.P.A. was on the staff, and Denys Wortman, and journalism in New York had an exciting quality about it, but Marquand felt that there was no future in newspaper work, that it was a horizonless grind. After he'd been on the paper a year, he bumped into Robert Benchley one night at the Harvard Club. Benchley told him of a job as copy writer at the J. Walter Thompson advertising agency. A competition was to be held for it. Marquand ran neck and neck with one of his war buddies, and both were taken on. Here was a new world, a world of vigor, push, drive, slogans, dollars — a hustling, bustling world, unlike anything in his experience. Advertising was the new giant loudspeaker of American free enterprise, the full-throated, blaring horn telling millions what to eat, what to drink, and what to wear, and doing it by the subtle arrangement of words. America was flexing her muscles after the war, and advertising was her wheat germ, her bodybuilder, her direct wire to the know-how that was to make her the finest, most glittering, best-oiled, and best-run productive machine on earth. The J. Walter Thompson people had some pretty big accounts — Yuban, Veedol, Tydol, Lux. Marquand wrote copy for an overall outfit, and did other chores about the office, but he was not happy, even though in later years he always insisted that the writing of advertising copy was more beneficial to a writer than newspaper work, since it dealt with basic fears and emotions. He had a strange desire "to write." It was neither entirely conscious nor entirely unconscious. He felt no particular dedication to style or form. When he thought about writing a story, the most important element seemed the telling of the story. One day in 1921, Stanley Resor, the president of the agency, said to him, "John, I don't believe you have the business instinct." Marquand was pleased beyond measure. He had saved four hundred dollars, a substantial sum in the year 1921, and he could now go off and write. He went first to Newburyport and stayed with his aunts, and then to Cambridge and stayed with a friend of his mother's. He had an idea for a costume story, a cloak-and-dagger novel, which he planned to call "The Unspeakable Gentleman."

7

The Leaves of Memory Seemed To
Make a Mournful Rustling
in the Dark

— HENRY WADSWORTH LONGFELLOW

CRAIG interrupted Marquand's thoughts. He leaned across the aisle of the parlor car, and said, "Tell me about your very first novel."

Marquand was ready for him. "Oh, no. I look back on it with horror," he said.

"I guess it was a foolish thing for me to ask about," Craig said. He sank back in his chair with such a defeated air that for a moment Marquand was tempted to talk to him. But then he returned to his thoughts of "The Unspeakable Gentleman."

He finished the novel, had it typed, and took it to Brandt & Brandt, the literary agents. They thought the story had merit, and sent it to the *Ladies' Home Journal*. The *Journal* bought it for two thousand dollars and ran it as a serial. At J. Walter Thompson's, Marquand had been making sixty a week, and the two thousand looked awfully big. "The Unspeakable Gentleman" began, "I have seen the improbable turn true too often not to have it disturb me. Suppose these memoirs still exist when the French Royalist plot of 1805 and my father's peculiar role in it are forgotten," and ended, many pages later, " 'Very much relieved,' he said, 'and yet — and yet I still feel thirsty. The rum decanter, Brutus.' " Marquand today found it difficult to read his earlier stories, and it was only with a good deal of will power, and rarely, that he ever did.

"The Unspeakable Gentleman" presented special problems and unique pains. A few nights after he finished his manuscript, he took it to the University Club, where he was meeting his old classmate George W. Merck. He and Merck started out together for an apartment house in the Thirties, on Park Avenue, where they were to call for some girls and take them to dinner. When Marquand entered the taxicab, he had the manuscript in a suitcase, which he placed in the doorless space alongside the driver (that's where they carried baggage in those days), and it was not until he stepped out of the cab that he realized, with a sudden wave of chill terror, that the suitcase had dropped off the cab. The manuscript was not found for ten days — ten terrible days for

Marquand — and then only after good old George had done some diligent private-detective work. Marquand was in despair and almost ready to abandon writing as a profession. He was never again to be without a carbon of his work.

The success of *The Unspeakable Gentleman* — it was published in book form by Scribner's after its magazine appearance — encouraged him to go on. The late George Horace Lorimer, then editor of the *Saturday Evening Post*, was enthusiastic about his work, and began to pay him five hundred dollars apiece for short stories. The late Ray Long, at that time editor of *Cosmopolitan*, who was not a man willing to see another editor develop a writer who seemed destined to reach popular heights, instantly began to compete with Lorimer. Lorimer responded, through Brandt & Brandt, with even higher rates. In those days, Marquand was just writing the best he could, and as rapidly as possible, and he aimed his products at the popular market without the slightest remorse. One lived and functioned as best one could.

Marquand's life now was to take a strange, and decisive, turn. While working in Cambridge, he had met Christina Sedgwick, the daughter of Mr. and Mrs. Alexander Sedgwick, and the niece of Ellery Sedgwick, the distinguished editor of the staid *Atlantic Monthly*. The Sedgwick family, although it came from Stockbridge, Massachusetts, where the frogs in the spring were all said to sing, "Sedgwick, Sedgwick, Sedgwick," was one of the intellectual prides of intellectual Boston — scholars, writers, teachers, ministers. They were among the select group who were final arbiters of taste. They were steeped in the traditions of the city, where American culture had been founded and had flourished, and they were nourished by their family traditions. They were a tightly knit group, proud, even arrogant, and to young Marquand from Newburyport and the *Saturday Evening Post* they had an indefinable, awesome quality. Marquand nervously crossed his legs in the parlor car. He tried to shake off his thoughts, but they persisted against his will. He rose and walked to the vestibule of the car, and stood for a moment looking out at the countryside of Rhode Island, but still the thoughts were with him. One can never dismiss some thoughts that lie most deeply within one; no effort of the will can do it. Christina, the mother of his first two children, was dead now. She had died not long ago — many years after she and Marquand were divorced. The marriage lasted nearly thirteen years, a tenderly happy and tenderly unhappy period for him. He tried to shake the thoughts off, but they would not leave. The period with Christina seemed so far away and yet so near, so much like an experience in a different, delicate world and yet so full of pain and anguish. One can never explain such things. And still they mean so much to a writer — not at the time, God knows, when only the happiness and pain are present, but later, in retrospect. Flashes of memory — scenes and incidents — passed through his mind with the very swiftness of the train that was taking him to Boston.

Christina was a fragile and exquisite, almost otherworldly, person, and Marquand had fallen deeply in love with her. They became engaged in Rome — a classic spot for such an event — in 1922. At the time, he was travelling abroad to look with fascinated eyes at the cathedrals and paintings he had had no time to observe during the war, and she was travelling with her parents. The Sedgwicks moved about Europe with quiet, unhurried, *fin-de-siècle* elegance. Wherever they went, they ran into other Sedgwicks, or collateral Sedgwicks, or, at the very least, people from Boston. Journeying with the Sedgwicks through Italy, looking with wonderment at the glorious relics, at the Tintorettos and the Raphaels, and joining up at the end of each day in some hotel lobby or restaurant with a group of understanding Boston people, Marquand sensed the meaning of Boston and the hold it had on its own kind and on the world. Boston meant a great deal to Marquand, more than he could say.

Marquand and Christina were married back in the States, after the tour. They were married in Stockbridge, at the church where her Uncle Theodore Sedgwick — who was rector of Calvary Church in New York — occasionally preached. They returned for the reception to the old Sedgwick mansion on the main street, a red house gracefully fronted by an elm-studded lawn. The scene came back to him sharply twenty-six years later, when his own daughter, also named Christina, was married in the same church and by the same Theodore Sedgwick. Marquand was embarrassed about going. He had not seen the Sedgwicks since he and Christina were divorced, and he felt that his presence might cause uneasiness among many. Still, his daughter insisted that he give her away, a request that he had no desire to turn down. "I will come, Christina," he told her, "but don't ask me to attend the reception." She agreed that he could slip away immediately after the church service. His daughter understood his feelings. There were many occasions after Christina's wedding when he thought about its fictional qualities: how he walked down the same aisle with his daughter, in the same church where he had been married, past pews filled with many people who had been at his wedding, seated upright and stately, and wearing on their faces that expression of solemn, half-expectant gaiety that one so often sees at weddings. Yes, it was an ordeal, giving Christina away, and when it was over, and Christina and her husband, Richard E. Welch, Jr. — he was a fine young man, with an excellent New England background, even if a year or so later he did absent-mindedly turn up one night at the Somerset Club wearing a tuxedo, green socks, and brown shoes — had been sealed in holy wedlock, Marquand was touched by the approach to his side of the elderly Ellery Sedgwick. He had rather thought that Ellery, who walked somewhat painfully with a cane, would avoid him. "John," Ellery said, "come back to the house with us. I want you to walk with me through the dog cemetery." Marquand said he would. It had been many years since he had walked through the Sedgwicks' dog cemetery, an ancient burial ground behind the house (the Sedgwicks themselves were buried elsewhere in town, in a pie-shaped burial ground known as the Sedgwick Pie; at the center lay an old ancestor, Judge Theodore Sedgwick, and other Sedgwicks surrounded him, their heads away from the center, so that when

they rose they would all face Judge Theodore),
clotted with small, well-tended graves, over which
stood minute, handsome headstones testifying in
Latin to the virtues of deceased Sedgwick dogs:
Zozo, Kai, Benvenuto Cellini — a series of ca-
nine celebrities going back more than a hundred
years and today resting in ancestral quiet. He and
old Ellery walked through the garden behind the
mansion — by that time rented from the Sedgwicks by a Stockbridge doctor, but put at the dis-
posal of the Sedgwicks for the wedding ceremony
— until they came to the dog cemetery. Ellery
suddenly spotted a fresh, unfamiliar grave among
the Cellinis. Two begonia plants stood beside a
tiny, makeshift headstone, and a small American
flag added a touch of poignancy to the scene. Ellery leaned heavily upon his cane and peered at
the stone, and his face became pale. He read
aloud the words on the headstone. " 'To
Tubby,' " read Ellery, " 'the cutest dog that ever
was.' " Ellery Sedgwick lifted his stick in the air
and brought it down upon the begonia plants.
"Blasphemy!" he cried. "Blasphemy!"

In a sense, that was part of the old Boston that
he himself had known when he was married to
Christina. He wished now that he could stop the
flood of thoughts, but there was no turning back.
He had done his writing at Wiscasset, in Maine,

and in Newburyport, and in Boston, and in an apartment in Cambridge, and in 1927 he and Christina bought a house on Beacon Hill, at 43 West Cedar Street — a lovely three-story place. He paid twenty-nine thousand dollars for the house, and he told the real-estate man he felt the figure was high. The real-estate man seemed wounded by the comment. "You can't go wrong on Beacon Hill," he told him. Marquand sold the house in 1938 for eleven thousand dollars. Assuredly, you *could* go wrong on Beacon Hill. Many things had gone wrong on Beacon Hill. There could be no more strained relationship for a writer than the one Marquand found himself in vis-à-vis the Sedgwicks. To the Sedgwicks, there was only one magazine, the *Atlantic Monthly,* and only one type of literature, spelled with a capital "L." Christina's mother never read anything that her son-in-law John wrote, and she was not ashamed to tell him so. He wrote serial after serial, hot and heavy adventure stories, stories of China, of the Civil War, of families in a small New England town. He worked long and hard, and made no pretensions whatever about his work, and felt no condescension toward it, either. Years later, he was to remark that he always did the best he could at whatever he was doing. The Sedgwicks' attitude hurt him deeply. They looked down upon him as a popular fictioneer, almost a pulp writer. One winter, he and his wife stayed with the Sedgwicks in Stockbridge. The house had a broad hall with doors opening off it. Marquand was working in one room off the hall, and Christina's brother, A. C. Sedgwick, was working in another, directly opposite. Marquand was applying himself to a serial, Sedgwick to a novel called *Wind Without Rain*. Mrs. Sedgwick rapped on Marquand's door one afternoon and asked him if he would mind stopping work and taking her son's dog, Chou-fleur, out for its midafternoon walk. "He's writing, you know," she said. That same winter, Marquand went down to New York and returned with a number of tropical fish. Mrs. Sedgwick was puzzled. "Why did you present us with tropical fish, John?" she asked. "It seemed a bit chilly up here," he replied. Mrs. Sedgwick was not amused.

Marquand did everything that was humanly possible to bring in as much money as he could. He soon found that marriage was difficult in Boston for a writer. First, a cook was required, then a maid, then a nurse, then many evenings with Boston society. But he thought he was doing pretty well, pretty well indeed. "I ruptured myself in those days with slave ships and Java

Heads," he remarked in later years. When his daughter Christina was a year and a half old, she had a bad bout of pneumonia, and then suffered a second attack of the illness. A rib had to be cut and the incision had to be drained, and she spent an entire winter in Children's Hospital, in Boston. Marquand worked feverishly on a serial called "Warning Hill" and received a thousand-dollar advance on it — a large sum, he thought — from Little, Brown. Before that, Scribner's had published nearly all his books, and the late Max Perkins had encouraged him, but Perkins' advances were somewhat meagre and he needed the money. (He had stuck with Little, Brown ever since.) In view of his industry, he was seriously hurt when one or another of the Sedgwicks would remark, "Why don't you write something nice for Uncle Ellery?" Write something nice for Uncle Ellery, indeed! And get paid handsomely with a check for a hundred dollars, and perhaps a silver inkwell!

And yet Boston charmed him in many ways. He worked at home, and ate his lunch at the Tavern Club, a men's club of considerable elegance, several mottoes of which make use of the word "bear," including "Bear with Us," and the symbol of which is a large stuffed bear. If one saw under the surface of Boston, one found that it had many wonderful qualities, many more than most American cities. He liked the notion of the Boston trustee — that unique Boston institution, perhaps closer to the notion of a London solicitor than anything else in this country. His own trustees, Welch & Forbes, took care of everything for him; he gave them an unrestricted power of attorney and they collected his royalties, paid his bills, handled ailing pets, and even bought him clothes on occasion. Their offices were austere, and contained a jawbone that had figured in the celebrated Dr. Parkman murder case — the firm had been Sohier & Welch then, and had represented Professor Webster — and overlooked the old burial ground off Park Street, where John Hancock lay, along with Paul Revere, James Otis, the mother and father of Benjamin Franklin, and old Sam Adams. (Old John Adams was buried in Quincy.) Marquand enjoyed his visits to the offices of Welch & Forbes; in fact, he enjoyed the company of Welch and Forbes themselves, two impeccably groomed young Boston men, souls of honor, with a sense of responsibility. He enjoyed hearing them say of him, "We are just hewers of wood and drawers of water for J. P. Marquand. We furnish logistic support to J. P. Marquand." He liked to look out over the old graveyard and recall that in the early days of Boston young sports

from the fine houses on Park Street would emerge
at night and sit on the tombstones, drinking
champagne.

The Somerset Club pleased him, too, with its
fantastically good, and cold, sweet Martinis, its
corndodgers, its Madeira sauce with peppercorns,
for sea food, its third-floor sign reading, "This
watercloset for emergency use only; other water
closets available on the second floor." The Athenaeum, at 10½ Beacon Street, was a joy — a private library, the members of which owned shares
in it, where tea or bouillon was still served in the
afternoons: with three plain crackers, three cents;
with three crackers and cheese, five cents; with
one plain cracker and one sweet, three cents; with
one plain cracker and cheese and one sweet, four
cents; with extra sweet crackers a penny apiece;
and extra plain crackers two for a penny. He relished the sign that had been put up many years
ago in the Athenaeum and that read, "Copies of
Cosmopolitan are available for the duration of
the Coolidge articles."

When you came down to it, he supposed, Boston was an acquired taste. One had to know these
people in order to appreciate them — people like
good old Gardi Fiske, who was the only World
War I ace to fall out of an airplane, catch hold
of the rear struts, and clamber back aboard, and

who worried not at all about the hereafter, since, as he once remarked to Marquand, "I know the Bishop, who is up there, and if there are any good clubs, he'll get me in." Marquand marvelled at the manner in which aristocratic Boston conserved the principal of its acquired wealth, and marvelled as well at its public spirit and its lack of extravagance or vulgar display of affluence. There was no shame in dressing tackily. Why bother about a run in one's stockings, or an old hat? Everybody knows you can afford better. Boston was symbolized once for Marquand when he recognized an elderly couple who were standing by the newspaper-and-candy counter at the Back Bay station. He knew they had recently given a million dollars each to Harvard. When he saw them, they were, in a subdued but firm way, arguing; one wanted a package of peppermint Life Savers, the other a package of orange Life Savers. They could not settle on which one to buy. Yes, there were times when, returning to Boston, just as he was doing now, he wished that he were living there again, even with all the memories. He knew the old feeling. He would look at the Esplanade, or walk through the Public Garden or past the Somerset, and he would think of the quiet of Beacon Hill and wonder why he didn't live there again. And then, if he stayed any time at all, the feeling of restlessness would start up. Something about Boston, perhaps its conservatism, perhaps its holding on to old ideas and its antagonism to new ones — the very things he loved about the place — would turn him against it, and within ten days or two weeks, like a man being smothered under a blanket, he would struggle desperately to get out. And he could not help remembering, although the thought pained him greatly, how he said to Christina, while they were still married, that he would like to — had to, in fact — write a book someday about Boston and the Boston type. He was thinking of a man to be called George Apley. Christina looked at him, startled, and said quietly, "We'll have to leave Boston, of course."

The porter gently tapped Marquand on the shoulder. "Back Bay station," he said. Marquand rose from his seat, and he and Craig stepped down onto the platform. "Mr. Marquand," said Craig as they picked up their bags and headed for the street, "I wish that sometime you would tell me a little something about Boston." Marquand smiled a peculiar smile. How could he ever tell him? How could he ever tell anybody?

8

You Might As Well Observe the Rules

MARQUAND began to feel like himself
— or what he thought might conceivably be himself, since one never really
knows — only when he and Craig arrived at
Kent's Island, his place outside Newburyport.
The day had been a wearing one. The train ride
had been something of an ordeal. The flood of
memories and feelings had wearied him. They
had left the train at the Back Bay station, and
Marquand had carried his suitcase and golf bag
to the street. He had been determined not to let
a redcap get his hands on them. Not this time.

Mr. Berry had been waiting for them in the
parking space at the Back Bay station with the
Buick. Mr. Berry was a countryman and had the
countryman's tall, hardened, outdoor look about
him. He took care of Marquand's place and occupied a house on the grounds, with his family.

Marquand was fond of Mr. Berry. He admired Mr. Berry's skill with domestic animals and with the land. He occasionally resented Mr. Berry's skill, not in a serious way but as a measure of what he regarded as his own inadequacy. This would arise when he took his two small sons out on the Parker River, near their home, in the motorboat, and the motor would go dead. Marquand was a man who loved machinery, and the working of machinery, in a purely intellectual way. He loved to have the working of machinery explained to him, but he had little inclination to work it himself. And so when he and the two little boys would start off on an adventure down the Parker River and the motor would go dead, Marquand would stare at the damn thing and swear silently (he could swear with magnificent variety, but he restrained himself in front of the boys) and be completely frustrated. Then it was necessary to row to shore and abandon ship and tramp through the salt hay to a telephone, and, in a voice that betrayed burning indignation, ask Mr. Berry to come down and fix the damn thing.

Mr. Berry had greeted Mr. Marquand at the station with the splendidly polite insulation of the countryman who works for the city man. In his every move, Mr. Berry revealed his independence, an independence Marquand deeply respected.

Marquand often pondered the relationships between people. They were difficult enough at best,
God knows, but especially difficult when someone
worked for someone else and had his residence
on the same grounds. The difficulty had become
acute, in Marquand's mind, when Mr. Berry installed a television set. Marquand would not
have one in his house. The two little boys and
his young daughter — he suddenly missed the
children and wondered what sort of mischief they
were up to down in Greenwich — had wanted to
go over to the Berry house and watch "Howdy-
Doody" and some other late-afternoon absurd-
ities, and the Marquands had forbidden them to
go. Marquand worried about this a good deal.
He hoped he had not hurt the Berrys' feelings.
He was a man who passionately wished not to hurt
anyone's feelings.

Marquand had introduced Craig to Mr. Berry
and, once they were settled in the car and had
started driving off to the Somerset Club, on
Beacon Street, for lunch, inquired after Daisy, one
of the cows. Was she giving milk? Not too much,
said Mr. Berry. And the new wing on the house
— it was finished, wasn't it, and the papers had
been cleared off the floor, and the spatterwork put
in? They had, said Mr. Berry, they had indeed,
and he felt that Mr. Marquand would be satis-

fied. As for news of Newburyport, there wasn't too much since his last visit, some weeks before. Still some talk about the old doctor's will, and who would get the tool chest and the bees — an item of current local interest.

Yes, the sight of Kent's Island was a welcome one at the end of a long and wearing day. Marquand had taken Craig to lunch at the Somerset Club, where Craig, as Marquand had predicted to himself, ordered the wrong thing. Craig had ordered *omelette aux fines herbes,* a damn-fool thing to order at the Somerset Club, which had some of the finest food in the East — and especially when Minced Chicken Sam Ward was on the menu. Then Marquand had taken him to the Boston Athenaeum for a short visit, and they had had an agreeable chat with Mr. Whitehill, the librarian, an impressive figure of a man with a round face and a huge, drooping mustache. Mr. Whitehill was the scholarly Boston type. Marquand had admired, as he admired so often on his visits to the library, a portrait, in the librarian's office, of a Hawaiian king, Kamehameha the Great, who was wearing a red waistcoat, and he had asked that they be taken into the Oval Room, where he pointed out to Craig the locked bookshelf containing many of the books from the library of George Washington. Mr. Whitehill had smiled faintly and remarked that in *The Late George Apley* Mr. Marquand had had Apley write a letter to his children in 1912 in which he mentioned an Apley family portrait that hung in that room. "Highly amusing," Mr. Whitehill had said pleasantly, "but I must point out that this room was not built until 1913. I yield to no man, of course," he had added hastily, "in my appreciation of the book as satire." Marquand had apologized for the error, and had then taken Craig over to the offices of Welch & Forbes, where he discussed business matters for a few minutes. Mr. Forbes, with whom Craig spoke briefly, had said that he considered himself and his partner "hewers of wood and drawers of water for J. P. Marquand," and Mr. Welch, with whom Craig also spoke briefly, had said that the firm was proud to "furnish logistic support to J. P. Marquand."

Marquand, Craig, and Mr. Berry then drove to Newburyport, along a new, broad, white highway, which, cutting through the heart of old New England, was dotted with signs advertising red-coach grills, ship's grills, jalopy races, fried clams, and cabins with steam heat, radios, and showers. One aspect of New England that even the most modern highway and the deepest-fried clam could not eradicate was the large number of cemeteries along the road — more cemeteries than Craig, who was a New Jersey boy himself, had ever before seen in the course of a thirty-mile ride. Since Marquand was absorbed in his own reflections, Craig permitted his mind to dwell upon the cemeteries, and he made a mental note to ask his superiors at *Sweep* to let him write a big, comprehensive article on the graveyards of New England sometime. He would call it "Buried History," and it would take in just about everything in New England life. But of course he knew he would never do anything about it. Mr. Berry interrupted Craig's and Marquand's thoughts by calling to Marquand from the front seat that he had heard a radio version of one of Marquand's Mr. Moto stories a couple of nights before, and that the author had been referred to as "James P. Marquand." Marquand said, "Damn! How ridiculous! I'll have my agent look into it," and he asked Mr. Berry if he would mind stopping for a minute at the Myopia Club. He wished to leave his golf bag there.

Marquand was exceedingly fond of the Myopia Club. There was a porch at the club for men and another one for women, and heaven help the women if they crossed the men's porch during restricted hours. Children were not allowed on the men's side of Myopia, and Marquand had once

broken the rules by installing one of his little boys
on the porch outside the bar while he went inside for a moment, and one of the older members
had raised Cain about the infraction. Marquand
had been wrong, no doubt about it. One observed the rules of Myopia because one respected
Myopia, and it was an institution of the North
Shore. Marquand stayed somewhat aloof from
the other members, a good many of whom looked
upon him with the suspicion they reserved for anybody in "the writing game," as they put it. They
suspected, perhaps with justice, that they were
just more grist to his mill — that he observed
them with considerably more astuteness than they
observed him. Of course, they failed to realize
that Marquand needed the nourishment of Myopia in order to write about it, even in a satiric
vein, for one had to love something solid, real,
and permanent before one could bring oneself to
satirize it. This escaped them. To them, Marquand was a man who lived by creative talent,
and therefore, in a sense, was an outsider, but
they were proud to know him and to say that
they knew him. Marquand had never fully for-
mulated his views about them. He enjoyed wearing
the canary-yellow-and-red tie of the club on club
occasions when the wearing of it was in order, but
he had a troubled realization that although this

was something he enjoyed, he also enjoyed writing about it humorously. He got great pleasure out of coming down from Newburyport two or three days a week to take golf lessons from the club's pro, John Thoren, but he would never go out on the links with the boys and play a round. Marquand had played only once on the Myopia course, which was well laid out and tough. He could do fifty up at Newburyport (nine) and about a hundred at Myopia (eighteen), and Mr. Thoren, a sharp-eyed, athletic fellow, held him in the highest esteem. Marquand, in turn, enjoyed the company of Mr. Thoren and the relaxation of coming down and getting away from his work and the children, and driving a few for the pro. "Mr. Marquand," Thoren would say when Marquand took a practice swipe at the ball, "that would have been great." Marquand would have come down every afternoon if Thoren had been able to accommodate him. Thoren, for his part, felt that Marquand was topnotch. "He's good for a man of his age," he would tell other club members. Thoren especially liked the way Marquand would cry out, when he hit at the ball and missed, "Put me down for a goddam son of a bitch!" Marquand liked the bar at the Myopia. There was no bartender; one simply took one's own liquor — all of it bearing the Myopia label, consisting of an alert fox and a hunting horn — out of one's own locker, and poured oneself a drink. Marquand had liked poor old Peter, now dead. Peter had been a steward, and he had liked Marquand and said of him, "I like Mr. Marquand. He doesn't fuss with his food." And Marquand liked the idea of belonging to a club that had as its oldest member Mr. Isaac Thomas, a great old Ipswichian, a portrait of whom, wearing a slouch hat and a tweed coat, hung in the big room, and who would throw the entire membership out of the room if their noise interfered with his watching of a baseball game on television. Today, Marquand did not speak to anyone at the club, because nobody was there. He merely left his bag.

As soon as the car had started up again, headed for Newburyport, Marquand began to speak of his small children. He was worried about their education. There were times when he felt they should be educated in Greenwich; there were times when he felt they should be educated in New York; there were times when he felt they should be educated at some school near Newburyport. Children needed roots. Certainly they could not have them on the streets of New York. A school near Newburyport will have to be it, he told Craig. They will love the winters in Newburyport, the high winds and the deep cold, and then the visible changing of the seasons. But he was worried about getting them to school. They could take a train, of course. No, a car and chauffeur will drive them down and bring them home. He added that the entire discussion might be academic, since Adelaide probably had some pretty firm notions of her own about their schooling. He promised himself to talk to her about it when he got back to Greenwich the next day. Mr. Berry turned off the road a few miles south of Newburyport and they passed through scrubby country. They were nearing Kent's Island, and Marquand was happier than he had been all day. He was, in a sense, coming home, although he knew that no place, anywhere, could guarantee happiness. When you came down to it, there was no place like home, wherever that might be. If it was at all.

9

A Great Many Good People Have Walked Over This Ground Ahead of You, Young Man

KENT'S ISLAND, where the Marquands lived during the summer and early fall, and where Marquand had written most of his novels, was not an island at all in the orthodox, romantic sense. One did not take a boat to Kent's Island, saying farewell to the shore behind and landing in a remote place. To reach Kent's Island, one drove through the scrublands for a while, crossed a small, rickety, and somewhat dangerous bridge of wooden planks thrown across a sluggish stream — at the point where the bridge crossed, it was nothing more than a tiny, lazy, meandering trickle — and there you were, on Kent's Island. Granted that the approach was unromantic, and that if you did not tell a person he was about to reach an island, he would assume that he was just crossing a small, rickety arrangement of planks and heading toward a country

89

estate, Kent's Island, for Marquand, *was* an island, even though technically it was an island only during high tide at the time of a full moon, when the marshes around it would fill up, and occasionally in the autumn, when the water would spill over the road and the salt spray would splash up inside one's automobile and possibly damage the motor.

After the Buick crossed the bridge, they could see Marquand's place ahead, amidst a clump of trees on a slight elevation — the main house, two stories high, magenta with gray-green trim; a barn across the road, and utility buildings behind; and a smaller house, where the Berrys lived, situated not far from the barn. Marquand told Craig that he had bought the place in 1935, and had built an addition to the main house in 1940. ("Let me get that down straight," Craig said, taking out his notebook. "The place itself in 1935, the addition in 1940." Craig put the notebook back in his pocket.) Marquand had been adding a little here, a little there, ever since. There were four cows, some rats, and no horses, he said. Suddenly the automobile slowed down almost to a crawl and, proceeding at this pace, gave a terrific lurch as it passed over a high bump in the road; it moved on a few yards, gave another lurch as it passed over another bump, and then lurched again. "Adelaide put those mounds in the road to protect the children from cars speeding up here," Marquand explained. "They will slow down the fastest-moving car. Adelaide likes to call it 'a Greenwich idea.' They know I don't like suburbia, and therefore they like to call this effective notion 'a Greenwich idea.'" The car passed two old-fashioned metal street lamps, the kind originally intended for gas, and stopped in front of the main house. Some lilac bushes were clumped beside the stone walk to the front door of the big house, which had charming, farmhouse proportions and an easy, graceful stretch of wings and other additions. It was a house that had been lived in — comfortable and unpretentious.

Marquand took Craig into the entrance hall, and it would have been apparent to Craig, if Craig had been that kind of person, that Marquand's love of detail in his books — his intricate descriptions of the insides of houses — was a reflection of his interest in the details of his own house. Taking Craig from room to room, some of them on a level slightly lower or higher than the adjoining ones, and all of them giving the impression of having been lifted from the American Wing of the Metropolitan Museum of Art, Marquand drew his attention to a number of the furnishings and pictures. Here was a portrait of some

ancestress, painted by Gilbert Stuart — a nice, re-
fined, pretty inhibited old girl with a lace doily
around her neck. Here was a dashing portrait of
Marquand himself, by Alexander James. Here
was a portrait of Hannah Gookin (Mrs. Richard
Kent), an original settler. Here was an oil called
"The Sister's Kiss," by Bouguereau. There was
an abundance of fine old furniture, what seemed
to Craig like dozens of Waterford glass decanters
on sideboards, and a collection of children's mugs,
some of them more than two hundred years old.
There was an old clock with a flag and an eagle
above its face, and there was an impressive picture
of Vesuvius erupting. Marquand told Craig that
he had sufficient knowledge of old American ships
to gather from the painting, which had a sloop
in the foreground, that the time of the picture
must have been around 1810. Some ship captain
had doubtless been in the Bay of Naples at the
time and watched the eruption, and ordered the
picture painted as a souvenir of the event. Craig
said he wouldn't know. Marquand led Craig
through another hallway — wings had been
added to wings — into what had formerly been
his study and was now a sort of trophy room,
decorated with souvenirs of his books and signifi-
cant events in his life. On the walls were framed
illustrations from the serial versions of *The Late*

George Apley and *Wickford Point* and *H. M. Pulham, Esquire*, a wooden model of an old Yangtze River junk, which he had bought in Shanghai and which was falling apart, and an intricately carved love stick and a mask from Truk, which he had picked up while he was in the Pacific during the last war. And there were family photographs all over the place. This old study of his was about to become the bar. He would move its present contents (he had *another* study, his *real* study, in another building, and he would show that to Craig later) to a room in the new wing, off the living room. The old study with the love stick and mask had turned out to be a passageway to the downstairs bathroom, and the little children had always been racing through and interrupting him. The new study, in the new wing, would prove a haven of quiet for reading. It had fine new bookshelves, and a desk, and plenty of heat from a Franklin stove — an idea of Adelaide's. By God, there was nobody who could fix a room up like Adelaide! There were four windows in it, too, so he could gaze out across the marshes at the tracks of the Boston & Maine Railroad in the distance. Adelaide, he said, did not like the idea of being able to see the tracks from the house. They didn't affect him one way or another.

Marquand suggested to Craig that they walk
about the grounds. They walked to a high spot
on the five-hundred-acre property, from which
one could see a mile and a half across the gentle
countryside to the sea itself. Marquand knew the
area well. He loved it, and he spoke lovingly of
it. In the old days, he said, the salt hay was used
for fodder. The earliest settlers had done well
with it. Marquand seemed almost completely relaxed now, and he walked in an easy, hunched-
forward manner, as though he had fallen into the
physical pattern of a man who was accustomed to
take long walks through open country. Standing
there, he looked like a squire in the Cotswolds.
He talked of the water problems at Kent's Island
— of how when they came there (owning a home
near Newburyport had long been a dream), there
were five or six wells on the property. They soon
discovered there was no water. Engineers were
hired, and they put in a contraption that, miracu-
lously, provided seven gallons of water a minute,
but the water was a thick broth as it emerged from
the faucets. As the next step — into his recita-
tion, Marquand interpolated cries of "Damn living in the country! Damn plumbers!" — the
engineers installed a huge, nightmarish object in
the basement, a thing with twisting wheels and
dials that resembled a badly designed submarine

engine room. That didn't work, either. Then the engineers came up with another idea — some tubes to be attached to the dials and wheels. At great expense, this was accomplished, and the water trickled through the tubes, and the manganese (that was what caused the trouble, manganese in the water) was removed, and — eureka! — they now had water. But something was always going wrong with the cock lock or something, or the pipes went crazy, and they abandoned the submarine wheels and dials, and found a new water supply, twelve hundred feet from the house and requiring expensive piping. It was all part of the burden of living in the country and of trying to plant a few roots. It was practically impossible to plant roots any more in America. There was either high overhead or social snobbery or remoteness from schools or general incompetence when it came to getting things properly fixed. Take tree surgeons. Marquand said that the damn tree surgeons would come out, climb a tree, poke around its branches as though they were listening for heart trouble, cut off a little here and a little there, and nothing but disaster resulted. They could find something when nothing was wrong. By God, that water thing, now he came to think of it, *had* exasperated him, and one day, after the new water supply had been discovered twelve hundred feet from the house, and the expensive piping had been installed, his friend Kenneth Roberts had come down with his divining-rod man, Henry Gross, and Mr. Gross had taken his magic stick and walked all around the place, holding it over the ground and talking to it in confidential tones, as though he were talking to an old, old friend. "Here?" Mr. Gross would ask the stick, and then he would say, "No? All right, over here, then. Ah, a little farther?" — and so on. Marquand had observed the scene with deep amusement, and when Mr. Gross announced that he had discovered water twenty feet below the ground, and only seventy-five feet from the house, Roberts had got so excited that Marquand thought his friend might be willing to put up the money to dig a hole and find out if water was really there. But Roberts had felt it was not his responsibility.

While telling of the water problem and the tree-surgeon problem, Marquand became ill at ease again. He had caught sight of a wire enclosure containing two beagles who were barking loudly and scratching wildly at the wire, and he walked over to it. "Why, those goddam dogs!" Marquand said, with some violence. "They don't even know their own names. Adelaide calls them David and Goliath, and they are quite stupid."

He stopped and looked at them contemptuously for a moment. "Stupid dogs!" he cried. They kept right on barking and scratching. "Really stupid dogs!" Marquand said to Craig. "I don't like beagles. I have two golden retrievers, Buster and Sandy, and *they* are *dogs.*" He told Craig that the sight of the beagles had upset him, they were so damn stupid, but he did want Craig to see his real study — a room that was part of the old woodshed, behind the barn, which had originally been the carriage house. It was here that he had written his novels, and he was quite sentimental about it. It gave him a sense of relaxation and repose. From its windows he could see — as Craig himself could see when they entered the square slate-blue room — the countryside all around, with its fences. They could not see the beagles and their nasty enclosure. It was the room of a cultured, solid, aloof, and disorderly but basically integrated man. There was much of the past in the room: a pair of Queen Anne chairs, a Jacobean rush chair (c. 1625), a clock that had been made on London Bridge, fine old blue plates commemorating General Lafayette's arrival at Castle Garden on the sixteenth of August, 1824, two pastels of the territory around Kent's Island, a very ancient desk with a secret drawer, a pine cabinet that had been salvaged from a beautiful

old house in Newburyport, a pine blanket chest
from Maine, a bust of Emerson — old Gardi
Fiske had given it to him, and because Gardi
Fiske had given it to him, he kept it. A low table,
not an antique, served as a desk, and there was a
green leather chair. There was a hooked rug on
the floor, and the rug had a profusion of browns
and blues in it. The old mingled with the new,
the past called to the present. All over the room
were books, papers, and pamphlets — books by
Plato, Hudson, Taine, Hazlitt, Galsworthy, Ra-
belais; books on China; *Who's Whos*; bulletins
from various banks; resort pamphlets; the short-
story collections of O'Brien; an *Information
Please Almanac*; and Justin Winsor's *Narrative
and Critical History of America*.

Marquand found some Scotch somewhere, and
he and Craig sat down to have a drink. Marquand
said nothing for a while. He seemed to be absorb-
ing the peace and quiet of his study, and the
memories of the room and what he had written
there seemed to be flooding through him. Craig
had no questions to ask; he was pleased just to be
there in the room with Marquand, and Marquand was too pleased at the moment to worry
much about Craig. He did worry a little, though,
about how this fellow Craig made out in his job.
"I suppose," Marquand said unexpectedly, "that

everybody on the *Transcript* when I was there wanted to write novels. They all wanted to write the Great American Novel. I didn't think much about writing until I left college. And then I was in newspaper work, and then the war came, and then I went into advertising, and I hated advertising. God, I hated advertising! I hated the notion of having to lick any goddam boss's boots. Perhaps writing springs from one's desperate desire to be independent, from the feeling that if one isn't oneself, one dies. This is my room, this is where I write, and this is the room I love. I never thought much about writing. I wanted my freedom from the nine-to-five grind, and when I graduated from that and was doing magazine work, I wanted freedom from the tyranny of plot, and so many words to a piece, and all that. Serial-writing is surrounded with obstructions and brakes that hold a writer back. I just wanted to be myself, I guess, and tell it the way I wanted to tell it."

Outside the study, it was growing dark. Craig, who had been drinking his drink rather too quickly, looked over at Marquand, seated in a high chair by a window, glass in hand, patrician head held high, and for a moment it seemed to Craig — although Craig knew that he could never put his impression down in words — that Marquand looked like an intensely intelligent boy

who had proved himself and was now enjoying
himself in the place where he had proved himself. Marquand had on his face a certain expression of pain — pain at what he had seen of the
world and the people in it — but he also showed
satisfaction at the observing role he had played.
Emboldened by the drink, Craig asked Marquand if he would take him over to Curzon's
Mill, where Marquand had spent so much time
with his maiden aunts as a boy. He knew that
Curzon's Mill was a source of some distress to
Marquand — that he had been involved in a bit-
ter fight with his cousins, the Hales (his paternal
aunt had married a Hale — Herbert Dudley
Hale), over the disposition of the property — but
he nevertheless asked if he could see the place.
A look of dismay passed fleetingly over Marquand's face. His clear blue eyes narrowed. He
rubbed his mustache reflectively for a second or
two, and then he said, "All right, let's go."

The journey was a hard one for Marquand.
The mill meant so much to him. In a sense, it
was his past, and although he denied that he had
based *Wickford Point* upon the neighborhood
around the Yellow House, the Red Brick House,
and the old mill, on the Artichoke River, which
constituted Curzon's Mill, it was difficult to believe that he had not unconsciously made this area,

which was so much a part of him, a part of the book. The two men climbed into the Buick and drove through Newburyport, past the site of Marquand's old schoolhouse; past the store of Mr. Davis, the druggist, who was in his nineties and still drove out to Salisbury Beach each Sunday at twelve miles an hour, holding up traffic for miles behind; past the Unitarian Church, with its beautiful white steeple, which Marquand had helped to restore. They drove out of town and several miles down the road, and Marquand pointed out the leaf-covered cemetery, wind-swept in the dusk, where his mother was buried, near many, many of his relatives. They drew up before the Yellow House, the front part of which had been built in 1782, as a hunting lodge for a man in Marblehead. It was sleepy and old, the Yellow House, and the big room in the rear with the bay window looked out upon the Artichoke River, and upon the Merrimack, too. The house had the smell of antiquity, and its rooms the quiet, indescribable air of places in which many people had lived many years. There was a peace pervading the Yellow House, the peace of the past. The old forsythia was still outside the door, and inside one could still see the four-poster bed Marquand's mother had slept in. The backgammon-and-domino room — the big one with the bay win-

dow — had the blinds drawn the way his great-
aunt, Aunt Mary, had wanted them drawn. Aunt
Mary's room was upstairs. "I was born here," she
always said, "and I hope to die here." And she
did. There were old pictures all over the place
— of the *Oregon* firing the last shot in the Battle
of Santiago Bay, with Admiral Clarke, a cousin of
his mother's, at the wheel, and pictures of the
family canoeing, and family, family, family por-
traits. Most important of all was the quiet, and
as Craig went up and down the twisting stairs,
and from room to room, with their mementos of
life lived and gone, he should have felt, but
didn't, that sense of the past that hung so heavily
over John P. Marquand and that, combined with
his acute observation of the present, had pro-
duced the writer of novels. Marquand, for his
part, said little, except to point out a knickknack
here and the sharp angle of a stairway there and
the banisters that had been added through the
years. He said he could remember that when he
was a boy he heard the slap-slap-slap of the sturgeon on the Merrimack River, and that his Aunt
Mary said she could remember the Indians pad-
dling across from Amesbury, on the other side,
and that John Greenleaf Whittier had come over
occasionally to read his works to Aunt Mary, on
whom he had a crush. Craig and Marquand

walked on the riverbank, along the untended path, past birch, white pine, oak, and red pine — the pines had blisters on them now — and saw the old boat landing, now unused, and the spot where Sunday-night suppers were once held. There was a rock, too, for picnics, but there were no longer any picnics. Had not an airplane suddenly wheeled above them, high in the sky, Marquand would have been almost overcome by the sense of the past, so lost was he in the memories of his youth.

If it hadn't been for that airplane, Marquand might never have been reminded of the present at all that late afternoon at the mill, and might never have thought about the fight over it. The fight had annoyed him. It had annoyed him terribly — especially the accompanying publicity. People should be permitted to have their family feuds in private, goddam it. He had had a row with his cousins, the Hales, and had gone to court over the ownership of the property. The Hales outraged him, and he outraged the Hales. They made a good deal of noise, and when they said they thought the old mill itself belonged to them — it was hard by the Yellow House, and had once been a tidal mill, grinding corn as the tide in the Artichoke rose and fell — the fight was on. Everybody in the family was sentimental about the

property, God knows, and Marquand was well
within his legal rights when he asked for an auc-
tion. The Hales knew he could outbid them.
(The legal business about who owned what parcel
of land in the property was too complicated ever
to be made clear to an outsider.) Marquand arrived in the Salem court with a derbied Boston
lawyer. The Hales turned up with a local attorney. Marquand took the case more seriously
than the Hales. He was wrought up about it. He
arose in court and delivered a few impassioned
remarks about the jungle creeping in on the
scenes of his childhood, but the court nevertheless awarded the mill to the Hales, and the two
houses — the Yellow House and the Red Brick
House — to him. But his heart was set on the
mill. He intimated that he might go to the Supreme Court of Massachusetts with the wretched
case, and the Hales knew that he could outlast
them financially. Finally, a settlement was made.
He got the mill and the Yellow House. They got
the Red Brick House. He said nothing of all this
to Craig as he took him into the mill — a striking
building, with an old mill wheel in the big room
upstairs, and beside it a new refrigerator, still un-
packed, which was awaiting the arrival of his eldest daughter, Christina, and her family. They
were going to spend the summer in the mill. He

could not bring himself to say anything at all to Craig about the mill. Either one loved its quiet and peace and sense of the past or one didn't. What could he tell Craig, anyway? And besides, it was dark outside now, completely dark, and the shades were drawn in the room with the bay window in the Yellow House, and Aunt Mary was gone, and one no longer heard the slap-slap-slap of the sturgeon on the Merrimack, and the pine trees were growing older and older, and he, John P. Marquand, home today on a mission, had to be at the Tuesday Night Club in ten minutes. He had almost forgotten about the paper he was to read. He had almost forgotten that it was the reason for his trip to Newburyport. He and Craig climbed into the Buick and sped back to town.

10

Gather Round, Friends

THE Tuesday Night Club had been organized December 16, 1911. It was one of the many New England clubs in which congenial friends with similar intellectual interests gathered to dine together and listen to a paper and engage in a discussion of the essayist's — to use the club's term — remarks. New England was dotted with such clubs, composed of earnest, thoughtful men. The members were carefully chosen, and family breeding played its proper role in determining a member's mental qualifications. The whole idea was a holdover from the Transcendentalist period and reflected New England's preoccupation with affairs of the mind. Other parts of the country could have groups that sang barbershop quartets or played poker until all hours, but New England still preferred to hear a paper on a topic of general interest. The Tuesday Night Club, which met every second Tuesday night at one or another member's house — the host served cocktails or punch and a buffet dinner — had been formed in rebellion against the Fortnightly Club of Newburyport, which also met on Tuesdays and which required its members to wear formal dress and served a sit-down dinner, without drinks. The Tuesday Night Club, branching off, had felt that a few drinks before dinner could not but aid the juices of the mind and produce somewhat better discussions. There was still another club in Newburyport — the Monday Night Club, which met on Wednesdays. Topics discussed at meetings of the Tuesday Night Club covered a wide range of human affairs — "Neighbors," "Józef Pilsudski," "New Frontiers," "Sheep Dog Trials," "Old Newburyport Industries," "Early Autos in Newburyport," and "One of the Greatest: A Life of Dante." Marquand, who became a member in 1938 — his father was already a member — had delivered a number of papers. One of them — "Where Are You, Prince?" — had been received with applause at its conclusion — the seventh time in the club's history, according to the minutes of the group, that a contribution had been so received. On another occasion, Marquand had discussed a trip he once took from Kalgan, in

China, just inside the Great Wall, through Inner and Outer Mongolia; he had discussed Ascension Island once, and Honolulu the same year ("a practiced, masterly hand," the minutes of the meeting recorded), and Hollywood, in a paper that had been pronounced, again according to the minutes, "an outstanding paper, amusing, informative, profane." The longest paper read at the Tuesday Night Club during its entire history had taken seventy-two minutes, and the shortest, a discussion of the first armored American warship, the Merrimac, had lasted only six. This evening, Marquand was to speak on "The Last American Plane from Peking." It seemed long ago — that yesterday afternoon in New York when he had dictated the paper to Miss Davis, talking swiftly, scraping at his mustache, pacing up and down the room, and when Miss Davis left, revising the paper in ink, in his small, almost illegible hand, chopping things out here and there and making it shipshape enough to be read aloud in an easy, carefree manner.

On the way to the meeting, which was to be held on this particular evening at the home of Mr. L. P. Dodge, at 106 High Street, Marquand told Craig that he was certain Mr. Dodge would serve, prior to the meal, a punch consisting of unsweetened pineapple juice, gin, and rum. He suggested that Craig watch how much he consumed, for the drink was considerably more powerful than it tasted. Marquand was right, of course. He and Craig arrived a few minutes after seven, and Mr. Dodge's quietly handsome antique sitting room — his was a two-story frame house, something of an anachronism on High Street, famous for its series of fine old Federalist mansions — was already filled with members, many with glasses in their hands. Among the people present were Mr. Dodge himself, a spare, tall man, a retired broker; Arthur P. Brown, also a retired broker; Laurence Hayward, a retired clergyman; Dana C. Wells, a short, white-haired gentleman and Marquand's old physics teacher at Newburyport High; Milton L. Dodge, a cousin of L. P., who owned several important patents on shoe machinery, and his son Allen A., who was associated with him in business; Morris B. Wood, a manufacturer of electrical appliances; Thomas M. Mercer and Edgar D. Dunning, teachers; Melvin F. Ames, Charles F. A. Hall, and Howard W. Rogers, doctors; James T. Connolly, a lawyer; and Charles C. Withers, the president of the Towle Manufacturing Company, a silverware concern and Newburyport's largest industry. They were engaged, when Marquand and Craig arrived, in the quiet buzz of friendly conversation that old friends fall into without difficulty. Nothing special was being said; acquaintances were being renewed after two weeks, or less, for most of the members had seen one another since the last meeting.

The evening went well. Marquand's face soon acquired a boyish flush. He was home, among his own, an honored novelist, a world celebrity, and while he relished the idea of speaking to the Tuesday Night Club, he still felt a youthful inability to believe that it was he, John P. Marquand, who had stood in this same Mr. Dodge's living room so many years ago and asked Mr. Dodge, in vain, for one of the Harvard Club Scholarships to Harvard. Now he was not only one of them but perhaps — and the thought was one he honestly wished to dismiss — perhaps one of the most celebrated among them. They liked him, they honored him, they were pleased to listen to his paper. The membership had its fill of unsweetened pineapple juice, gin, and rum. "Real New England rum, this is," Mr. Dodge told Craig, and then took him aside and told him about Marquand's having come to see him about the scholarship. The members repaired to the dining room, where a buffet dinner of chicken à la king, mixed salad, a rice dish with tomato sauce, almond pie, beer, and coffee was served. The members sat down at little tables, scattered about the room, or at the big table, in the center. The talk was easygoing. Some discussed old times in Newburyport, when sleighs went down High Street in the deep snow; others talked of present-day skiing nearby; the doctors discussed medicine, not in terms of recent scientific discovery so much as in terms of their individual practices and the local common colds. When dinner was over, everybody went back to the sitting room, and John P. Marquand, seated in a huge, high-backed chair, facing his friends and neighbors, who sat on chairs and sofas around the room, began to read his paper on "The Last American Plane from Peking." He read in a slow, measured, friendly tone. He was home, among friends. He was where he belonged, and his friends listened to his clear-cut, crisp, and yet sentimental narrative with deep attention. He told of Peking — a city he loved, as he said in the paper, for its great medieval walls, its mysticism and magic, its soothsayers, its *fêng-shui*, its variety of diversions, its rice cakes, its confectioners and barbers, its pageantry, its pavilions and palaces, its Temple of Heaven, its ancient bell tower and its imperial city. He said that the city from the air looked like a willowware plate. "The willows around the mud-walled farm villages," he said, "were coming into leaf, and in the air there was the faint smoky haze that exists even on the clearest day. It was the haze of the loess dust from Shansi and the yellow dust from the Gobi Desert, which have always blown over China since the hills were denuded of trees." He had been out there in 1947, with an admiral, and the admiral's main concern before their plane landed was whether the welcoming committee standing below on the airstrip were wearing neckties. The novelist in Marquand delighted in this thought; he twisted it and turned it and rounded it out. Then he told of having dinner, with plenty of warm rice wine, at the home of a General Li, whose interpreter turned out to be a Harvard man — '21. "When it appeared that I, too, had gone to Harvard," he said, "General Li said that I was his eldest brother, and the Mayor of Peking embraced us both."

The moment Marquand finished, his old physics teacher, Mr. Wells, who had been clocking the paper, cried out, "Thirty-two minutes!" Marquand sat back, beaming, and awaited the question period. Each person in the room was asked, in turn, what he thought of the paper. Each said that he thought it had been an exceptional picture of Peking. A number of them wished to know more about the language and culture of China, and Marquand, by now actually giving the impression that he was enjoying himself, talked on

and on, of street fakirs and theatricals, of the
blind storytellers, of the difficulties Chinese
scholars faced these days under the new regime,
of having been hit on the knee from behind by
a coolie at the airport. Without any fuss, the
members paid small, gracious, reserved compli-
ments to Marquand. They told him quietly how
fond of him they were; how glad they were that
he had gone out to the far corners of the world,
had written his books, and had brought back just
such knowledge as he had displayed this evening.
Marquand looked as gratified as a man receiving
an honorary degree from the college in his home
town. After all, it *was* something to have best
sellers behind one, to read a paper, to be among
friends, to have made good. And yet, Marquand
felt in his heart a sadness about the past. The
past was there, and the past was real, and it could
never be wiped out.

The meeting broke up about ten o'clock. The
members put on their hats and coats and walked
out the door of Mr. Dodge's house onto High
Street — a study now in black-and-white. The
fine old gleaming Federalist houses, with their
clean white fences and cupolas and widows'
walks, and their memories of a great seafaring day,
stood like watchmen in the night. Mr. Dodge, at
the door, whispered into Craig's ear. "If I had

known then what I know now," he said, "I would have given him the scholarship." And Craig, who was to return to New York, and to his wife and to his children, and who was to try and write about John P. Marquand — a man he could never understand, since human beings can never understand one another — looked at Mr. Dodge, and at Marquand, too, standing alone in the shadow of the great houses. He did not say, as he might have said, "Then perhaps he would not have written the novels." Instead, he merely said, "Thank you for a most enjoyable evening."

THE END